A Joke is Not Just For…

Bill Jessop and Shaun Rusk

A Joke is Not Just For…

Vanguard Press

A CIP catalogue record for this title is
available from the British Library.

ISBN 978 1 80016 853 4

*Vanguard Press is an imprint of
Pegasus Elliot Mackenzie Publishers Ltd.*
www.pegasuspublishers.com

First Published in 2023

Vanguard Press
Sheraton House Castle Park
Cambridge England

Printed & Bound in Great Britain

Contents

Foreword

Oprah... Stephen Fry... Barack Obama... Adele...

These are just some of the people who have not endorsed or even heard of our book!

Despite that lack of acclaim, this book is for all ages and occasions: whether it's a rib-tickling joke, a bon mot or a well-rehearsed 'off the cuff' wisecrack!

It is small enough to be read in one blast, or to be dipped into occasionally, especially ahead of a night out, so you are ready and waiting for the moment to impress!

How did the book start?

The 'Great Pause' has changed all of our lives, in more ways than one, and this book is no exception.

I can't remember... was it the first lockdown, no, the second... how many have we had? Either way, Bill Jessop, had time on his hands and began posting daily jokes on Facebook; and as those jokes multiplied, so did the thought of creating a book to spread the laughter to a wider audience.

Rugby and alcohol were in many ways the catalyst. In the bar after a Saturday match, with the merciless mickey-taking and joke-telling that takes place in every rugby club.

Instead of just a higgledy-piggledy mish-mash of jokes, we decided to try and place them into some sort order, or more specifically, subject area.

So enjoy our book. It will, hopefully, bring a smile and a laugh.

Stay well.

Bill Jessop and Shaun Rusk

ACTIVITIES

Today a man knocked on the door and asked for a small donation towards the local swimming pool.
So I gave him a glass of water.

-

I went to my yoga class, but the instructor was drunk.
I was put in a very awkward position.

-

If anybody would like to help me with my poor woodworking…
My door is always open.

-

Well, I'm now banned from the local pub quiz…
In retrospect I should have answered 'Fiji' when asked 'Where do women have the curliest hair?'

-

I got an email saying I had won a free fishing lesson.
Do you think there's a catch in it?

-

I intended to go bowling today but all the alleys were closed…
Something to do with a strike.

I was thrilled yesterday when I played darts blindfolded.
I never knew what I was missing.

-

I rang the local swimming baths and asked, 'Is that the local swimming baths?'
The person replied, 'It depends where you're calling from!'

-

I went to see the world's largest snooker set the other day.
It took a while to get in – the cue was massive.

-

I organised a March against Apathy…
But no-one turned up!

-

A troupe of Russian acrobats who perform human pyramids have had a member deported.
Now they don't have Oleg to stand on.

-

Our local vicar is helping out in the Royal Mail Sorting Office.
We call him 'Pastor Parcel.'

-

I went swimming today. I had to take a pee in the deep end.
The lifeguard noticed and blew the whistle so loudly I nearly fell in!

I went down to my local gym and asked if they could teach me to do the splits. The trainer asked, 'How flexible are you?'

I replied, 'Well, I can't do Tuesdays.'

-

I'm twenty hours into my sponsored semaphore marathon.

Unfortunately, I'm starting to flag badly.

-

In a pub, a bloke asked if I wanted a game of darts? I said, 'The nearest to bull starts.'

I said, 'Baa.' He said, 'Moo.'

I said, 'You start!'

ANCESTRY

Don't bother with those ancestry DNA kits.
Just announce you've won the lottery… then see how
many relatives you have!

BOOKS

First rule of Thesaurus Club: You don't talk…
Converse, discuss, speak, chat, deliberate, confer or gab
about it.

-

I was so bored today, I memorised six pages of the
dictionary.
I've learnt next to nothing.

-

I've just bought a book called, 'DIY house
construction,' by Bill Jerome Holmes.

-

I went to the library looking for books on oils and
lubricants.
The lady told me they were over in non-friction.

-

I'm attempting to write a novel about a broken compass,
but I'm not really sure where I am going with it.

-

I was trying to read a book on the history of Sellotape,
but I couldn't find the beginning.

I received disappointing reviews about a book I wrote about roof renovations.
It's been slated.

-

A book fell on my head yesterday. I only have my shelf to blame.

-

I was in a library looking for a book on how to make fire by rubbing two sticks together.
I found it in the friction section.

-

Amazon had a book titled: 'How to solve half of all your problems.'
So I bought two copies!

-

I belong to a gang called The Secret Five. We are sworn to secrecy.
It's so secret I have never found out who the other four are!

-

You cannot 'run' through a campsite because it's past tents.

-

I just found out that I'm in the Guinness Book of World Records for the most items hung on a washing line…
It was a lot to take in.

CHRISTMAS

I've put mistletoe up to get into the Christmas spirit.
Some people in the office urinal seemed uneasy though.

-

A copy of 'A Christmas Carol' fell on my toe...
It hurt like the *Dickens*!

-

A survey has concluded that wives who put on weight
at Christmas live longer than husbands who mention it.

-

I'm bringing out a version of the Band Aid song, 'Duvet
Know It's Christmas?'
It's a cover!

-

Merry Christmas everyone! Don't forget to wind back
your scales by three kilos at midnight!

-

Christmas is finished, and my resolution is to stop using
spray deodorants...
Roll on the New Year!

Just bought my tickets for the Reincarnation Society Christmas Party.
They're having a soul night!

-

Just got a Christmas Humpty Dumpty from Aldi.
It comes with Aldi king's horses and Aldi king's men.

-

I went to Cash Converters yesterday to raise money for Christmas.
They gave me £5,200 and never even took the gun!

-

It's sad that some schools are no longer performing Nativity plays. It stops children from having the opportunity to eat, drink and be Mary.

-

I'm overcoming my Christmas food addiction...
I'm going cold turkey!

-

Got a Christmas card today and a Yorkshire pudding fell out. It was from my Aunt Bessie.

-

I asked my young god-daughter what she wanted for Christmas. She said she liked 'Frozen,' so I bought her a pack of Birds Eye peas.

-

I've just bought a Christmas tree. It was too tall for the car so I cut the top off...
I always wanted a convertible!

At the Christmas meal, my serviette started singing, 'Chestnuts roasting on an open fire...'
Sung by Napkin Cole!

-

Christmas tip: Don't buy a Microsoft Advent calendar. Every time you open a window, it shuts again.

-

At Christmas, there always seems to be one weird relative at the table. If you don't know who it is... it's probably you!

-

My Christmas jumper keeps picking up static electricity. I exchanged it for another one – free of charge.

-

I went home and found all the windows open and everything gone.
That's the last time I buy an Advent calendar!

-

Good news for insomniacs – only three more sleepless nights till Christmas!

-

I'm in trouble with my wife again. I bought her some lorry oil for Christmas.
Apparently it's pronounced 'L'Oreal!'

CLUBS

I had to stand up at the Kleptomaniacs Anonymous meeting last night as all the seats had been taken.

-

I'm starting an Atheist Club. It will be a non-prophet organisation.

-

Last week I started a club called Exaggerators Anonymous. We already have seven million members!

-

I was going to attend the Paranoids Anonymous meeting, but no-one would tell me where it was.

-

Unfortunately, after many years as head of the British Stilt-Walking Society, I am stepping down.

-

My friends have started a Chinese Burns Club.
I wasn't keen on joining, but they twisted my arm.

-

Last week, at the Liars Club, a bloke was telling me how he had slept with a thousand women. I had told him a million times not to exaggerate!

My application for membership of the Woodworkers Club was refused. They said I couldn't join.

-

I'm thinking of starting a local support group for insomniacs. There seems to be a lot of people up for it.

-

I've just joined Paranoids Anonymous. We never meet just in case anybody spies on us.

-

I went to my first Arsonist Support Group meeting last night. We all got on like a house on fire.

-

The residents are having a meeting about some weirdo who lives on our road...
I'm still waiting for my invite.

-

I rang the Paranoid Support Line earlier, but they didn't answer...
I think they're ignoring me.

-

I joined a new club for pessimists last night. It wasn't a great success - the room was half empty!

CULTURE

Woke society demands that the next James Bond will start off as a man and transition to a woman.
The film will be called 'Cocktopussy'.

-

You won't like me when I'm angry... I always back up my rage with facts and documented sources.
I'm the Credible Hulk!

-

The condition of the man who was mauled at the Teddy Bears' Picnic is said to be improving...
But he's not out of the woods yet.

-

In America they have elevators, but in the UK we call them lifts.
I suppose it's because we are brought up differently.

DATING

I met a girl who loves palm trees. We had our first date last week.

-

My mate joined a Ukrainian dating site. He's now got a chicken Kiev.

-

'I'm not saying your perfume is too strong. I'm just saying the canary was alive before you got here.'

-

I've just finished a graph charting my past relationships. It has an Ex-axis and a Why-axis.

-

I've learnt two main lessons in life:
1) If you love someone, learn to let them go.
2) I'm not cut out to teach rock climbing.

-

If you fancy a farmer's daughter, you better do something to a tractor!

-

I've just established a dating site for chickens. It's not a full-time job, it's just to make hens meet.

I used to date an air stewardess from Helsinki. I dropped her off at work one day and she just vanished into Finnair.

-

I was supposed to go on a date with an architect tomorrow, but she cancelled.
She already had plans.

-

I was dating a woman who was obsessed with collecting magazines. We split because she had too many issues.

-

I've got a date with a girl who makes wheelie bins but I don't know what day to take her out!

-

Breaking up with an optician is hard. When you tell them you can see them anymore, they move a bit closer and say, 'How about now?'

-

I once dated a tennis player, but we split. Love meant nothing to her!

DICTIONARY

Sarcasm and orgasm are my favourite '-asms.'

-

Cleanliness is next to godliness... That's the last time I buy a dictionary from Poundland.

-

Rats are under rated... Just check your dictionary!

-

If I ever find out what a 'spoonerism' is... I'll heat my cat.

-

Why do so many people get simple sayings wrong? Please send your answers on a coast guard.

-

I'm looking for a pun about carpentry. Does anyone know one that woodwork?

DRINK

I once read an article about the perils of drinking. It frightened me so much, I gave up reading!

-

A control-freak goes into a bar and orders everyone a round.

-

I always take life with a pinch of salt... and a slice of lemon... and a shot of tequila.

-

The worst pub I've ever been to was called The Fiddle. It was really a vile inn.

-

A dung beetle walks into a bar and asks, 'Is this stool taken?'

-

I drink wine because my doctor told me my health would improve if I didn't keep things bottled up!

-

Fourteen muscles are activated when opening a bottle of wine... Follow me for more fitness tips!

I enjoy a glass of red wine each night for its health benefits. The other glasses are for my witty comebacks and flawless dance moves!

-

A blind man walked into a bar... then a table... then a chair...

-

Drinking alcohol can cause memory loss, or even worse... it can cause memory loss.

-

People say my homemade wine tastes like vinegar. I think it's just sour grapes.

-

A weasel walks into a bar. 'Wow,' said the bartender, 'I've never served a weasel before. What can I get you?' 'Pop' goes the weasel.

EDUCATION

I was at school with a lad who spent all his time counting. I wonder what he's up to now?

-

My geography teacher once asked me what I knew about Damascus. I told her that it killed 99% of all known germs.

-

Question: Is it OK that I start drinking as soon as the kids are at school, or does that make me a bad teacher?

-

I am a big fan of whiteboards. I find them re-markable!

-

In retrospect, I should have known I had failed my Braille exam… it just felt all wrong.

-

I went for my first yodelling lesson. We were told to form an orderly, orderly, orderly queue.

-

I didn't really want to go on the lasso making course… but I got roped in!

I've just started an archaeology course and I'm really digging it.

-

I accidently booked myself on to an escapology course. I'm really struggling to get out of it.

-

I did really well on the first day of my levitation course. I went straight to the top of the class.

-

I've decorated my lounge with desks, chairs and a blackboard. I think it looks classy.

-

I've just started an engraving course.
There's lots to learn but we've barely scratched the surface so far.

-

I failed my audition at the mime school. I guess it could have been something I said.

ENVIRONMENT

I've just had my solar panels nicked. It's daylight robbery!

-

Did you know, if the whole human population held hands around the equator... quite a few would drown.

-

I was going to climb Mount Everest, but instead it will be Mount Kilimanjaro...
Something to do with 'climb it change.'

-

I've just moved into an eco-flat that's been built out of recycled coffee beans. I'm on the ground floor.

-

I've just been visited by the Plastic Mafia. They made me an offer I can't reuse.

-

Red sky at night... parts of the electromagnetic spectrum reflecting off dust particles in the ionosphere. Red sky in the morning... same!

-

I'm writing a book about hurricanes, tornadoes and whirlwinds. It's only in the draft stage at the moment.

The safety inspector turned up at our nuclear plant to carry out an assessment. Hopefully it doesn't get a glowing report.

FAMILY

I come from a family of failed magicians. I have two half-sisters.

-

I'll never forget my granddad's last words:
'Are you holding that ladder tightly?'

-

My granny stood by my granddad for forty-six years.
They only owned one chair.

-

My young son swallowed a fifty pence coin. He was rushed to hospital for an operation.
Afterwards the doctors told us there was still no change.

-

I was told I had my father's ears…
That was the strangest will I've ever read!

-

Vocabulary is so important…
If I had known the difference between 'anecdote' and 'antidote,' Granddad would still be alive.

-

I haven't seen my brother since we left Australia. We were separated at Perth.

The unluckiest person in my family is my uncle. Two weeks after he went blind, his guide dog went deaf.

-

My brother used to go out with an undercover cop called Rose. She was a plant.

-

My granddad was a glazier. He once repaired forty-six broken windows in a day, before realising he had a crack in his glasses.

-

What do you say to your sister when she's crying? 'Are you having a 'crisis!''

-

I posted my sister's birthday card yesterday and I thought, 'What a waste of £2… But you never know if you'll need a kidney!'

-

I asked my clumsy brother if he's stopped sniffing glue, but his lips are sealed.

-

I tried some goat milk and it was really good. It took me back to when I was a kid.

-

My dad used to let me put my pocket money in a special box under the stairs. It wasn't until I was fifteen that I found out it was the gas meter!

My sister is single and works for British Gas, if you wanna meter?

-

My mum put food on a spoon and said: 'There's a train coming!' I ate it because if I didn't, she would leave me on the railway line.

-

When I was a boy I asked my dad, 'Can I use the lawnmower to make extra money?'
'Of course,' he said. So I sold it!

-

I knew I wasn't loved as a child when my parents asked me to help arrange a surprise birthday party for my twin brother!

-

My kids have been throwing Scrabble tiles at each other. It's all well and good until one of them loses an I.

-

When I left home, my mum said to me, 'Don't forget to write.'
I thought, 'That's unlikely, it's a basic skill.'

FATHER TIME

There are three signs of old age:
First are wrinkles, second is memory loss and third...
are wrinkles.

-

The inventor of Jack-in-the-Box has died. His funeral
will be a very tense occasion.

-

Just got back from my mate's funeral. He died after
being hit on the head with a tennis ball...
It was a lovely service.

-

The inventor of the snooze button has passed away. His
funeral is Monday at 6.30... 6.45... 7am.

-

My memory is getting bad. It was only when I couldn't
find my own allotment that I realised I'd lost the plot.

-

Breaking News: The man who invented throat lozenges
has passed away. There will be no coffin at his funeral.

-

The man who invented predictive text has died...
His funfair is next monkey. May he rust in piss.

FILTHY LUCRE

The cashier told me: 'Strip down facing me.' By the time I realised she meant the debit card, it was too late.

-

My credit card bill arrived with the wrong name on it. Apparently I'm Max Stout!

-

I'm trying to give up my obsession with ATMs, but I'm getting withdrawal symptoms.

-

My bank phoned me about suspicious activity on my account. They don't believe I bought a gym membership!

-

I thought about putting my jokes on the financial markets, but in retrospect, they would only end up as laughing stock.

-

Banks should try harder to keep their ATMs machines full. I've been to five today and all had 'insufficient funds.'

FOOD

I had a text from Cadbury's today. I ignored it, it was just Flake news.

-

I bought some Jelly Babies in Aldi. I'm a bit disappointed they were not called 'Aldi Young Dudes.'

-

I've started telling people about the benefits of eating dried grapes. It's about raisin awareness.

-

What's worse than finding a worm in your apple? Finding half a worm!

-

I bought a Womble pepper grinder today. It's useless, everything is either underground or overground.

-

I said to the baker: 'How come your cakes are 50 pence, but that one is £1?'
He said: 'That's Madeira Cake!'

-

I don't know why people love jam sponges so much. Mine made a real mess in the bath.

I made a mistake at the supermarket today. I was supposed to get six Sprites, but accidentally picked 7up.

-

I nearly got caught out on the 'Weight Watchers' website. It asked if I accepted cookies!

-

My granddad was a greengrocer. When he retired he got a final celery pension.

-

I've recently become a part-time fruitarian. I can only eat things that fall from trees. I've just had an Apple and Squirrel sandwich for lunch.

-

I just had a windfall on some lamb burgers. It turns out they were minted!

-

I was watching an Australian cooking show and the audience clapped when they made meringue. Strange, I thought they would boo-meringue!

-

I've just bought eight venison legs for £40… is that two deer?

-

I really shouldn't have eaten that liquorice before bed. It made me dream all sorts.

-

I feel so down at the moment… I had Ordinary K cereal for breakfast.

Anyone who says an onion is the only vegetable to make you cry has clearly never been hit in the face with a turnip!

-

This is the fifth time this week that I've skydived into a bakery… I'm on a roll.

-

I'm so lucky. My wife loves to be covered in cheese… she's a real cracker.

-

I went out for a meal last night. I tried a pelican burger. It was lovely, until I saw the size of the bill!

-

I was sure I'd eaten that mustard before… I guess I was having Dijon Vu.

-

I named my chicken restaurant after my grandchildren, Sam and Ella. I'm not sure why it's not doing well.

-

Red wine and fish really don't mix. In fact, mine died!

-

I complained to the Waitrose manager when I found a loaf of bread for £4. She said that many items went into it. Hopefully, one of them is a £2 coin!

-

I'm investigating somebody who poured gravy over my allotment for the last few nights… The plot thickens.

When I was struggling for money, I worked at Pizza Hut. I kneaded the dough.

-

Pre-cooked bread... Now that's a half-baked idea!

-

I was invited to a party by a friend. When I got there, I threw my keys into a bowl in the middle of the table. Everyone just looked at me; I had ruined the trifle.

-

Just burned 2,000 calories. That's the last time I leave brownies in the oven while I nap.

-

My Indian food was delivered by an elderly lady who told me I was gorgeous. She was my complimentary naan!

-

I was going to have some 'rocket salad' for lunch today, but it went off before I could eat it!

-

Imagine you are halfway through eating a horse, when you think, I'm not as hungry as I thought I was!

-

My mate asked me to buy some olives. When I asked what kind, he told me to get stuffed... How rude!

-

I went for a job as a sandwich maker, but sadly no luck. The roll had already been filled.

Apple has said that although their profits are down, their turnover is still good.

-

I think the 'alphabetti spaghetti' I ate has upset my stomach. I had a very large vowel movement.

-

I think the roast beef I had on Sunday was actually horse… It's given me the trots!

-

I put blood, sweat and tears into everything I do. That's probably why my restaurant was shut down.

-

Sick of people moaning about my bread making technique. I really don't knead it!

-

I've just started on the Middle Eastern cannibal diet. I start the day with a breakfast sheikh.

-

I warned my friend not to open a pastry shop without any experience. It's been a year now and he's still struggling with his turnover.

-

I went to an open-air café yesterday, but unfortunately it rained… it took me four hours to finish my soup!

-

I saw a burger van today that was properly upmarket. It had four Michelin tyres.

I'm a bit worried. Last night I accidentally ate some foil wrapped food... Will I sheet metal?

-

I was in a restaurant when a prawn cocktail hit me on the head. I looked around and this bloke shouted: 'That's just for starters!'

-

Just had a nice piece of cheddar from Israel. I love cheeses of Nazareth!

GAMBLING

Just met a chap called Paddy Power. What are the odds of that?

-

I rang Gamblers Anonymous this morning, but they were very busy. They told me to ring back at 20 to 1.

-

I had a bet with a bloke who said I couldn't name a famous Egyptian landmark. I thought, that's what you Sphinx.

-

We went out for a meal tonight. I had a rare steak. The waiter asked me if I wanted anything on it? I thought for a moment and replied "a fiver each way!"

-

I placed £50 on a horse named 'Creosote' at Cheltenham today. I asked, 'Is it any good?' The bookie replied, 'Well, it's great over fences!'

GEOGRAPHY

If there's one place on this planet I really can't stand…
it's ice skating rinks!

-

Did you know there are no canaries on the Canary
Islands? Same with the Virgin Islands… No canaries
there either.

-

The hardest thing about living in Mexico is you need
50,000 other people to wave to someone.

GODLY

A bloke driving a tractor was shouting, 'The end is nigh…'
I think he was Farmer Geddon!

-

I wanted to become a monk, but I never got the chants.

-

How do you make holy water? You boil the hell out of it.

-

I got fired from my job at Ancestry.com. I was asked, 'How do I find my ancestors?'
'Try a shovel.' wasn't the right answer.

-

When I was shopping yesterday a Hare Krishna follower waved smoking sticks over me… I was incensed!

-

I've seen a dishevelled nun walk past my house recently. I stopped her one day and asked, 'Why so scruffy?' She said, 'I've got into bad habits.'

I'm restoring an old church. If anyone wants to help, they can give me a bell.

-

I thought about asking God for a bike, but I knew God doesn't work that way... So I stole a bike and asked for forgiveness!

-

When I got baptised, the priest wore a false beard and moustache... It was a blessing in disguise.

-

I was christened with a flamethrower... that was a baptism of fire.

-

Sadly, the person who invented Tupperware has died. The funeral was delayed as they couldn't find the correct coffin lid.

-

A Dutchman had inflatable shoes. One day he went for a run and popped his clogs!

HEALTH

Is it normal for my left nipple to be larger than the other two?

-

Conjuntivitis.com: That's a site for sore eyes.

-

I was excited when my wife suggested we play doctors and nurses. I didn't expect to be left in the hallway for two days.

-

I used to have an invisible Japanese friend, but it was just my imagine Asian!

-

I hate that feeling after surgery when you're not sure if you're awake or asleep... or even if you have operated on the right patient!

-

My doctor says I am much happier since I changed from coffee to orange juice in the morning because of all the extra vitamin C... I think it's just the vodka!

-

I've decided I'm going to live forever... So far, so good!

If anybody wants a copy of Osteopath Weekly, I have back issues.

-

I went to see my doctor. He asked me to provide a stool sample. I was a bit irritated, but I thought OK… so I've enrolled on a woodworking course.

-

My mum fell on the floor and so I phoned the hospital. I said, 'My mum has collapsed.'
'Do you want a stretcher?'
I replied, 'That will just make her worse!'

-

The doctor told me I had hypochondria. I thought, 'Not that as well.'

-

Everyone was excited at the Autopsy Club… It was open Mike night!

-

My doctor has diagnosed me with low blood pressure. To correct it, he suggests I buy two IKEA self-assembly wardrobes!

-

Research says laughing for two minutes is healthier than jogging for an hour, so I'm sitting in the park laughing at all the joggers!

-

Apparently, if you measure the length of your fingers, it can tell you… how long your fingers are!

Well, I 'm back from A & E… but a word of warning! The Dyson Ball Cleaner is not what you think!

-

I said, 'Doctor, I feel the whole world is against me.' He said, 'Hold on a minute… Hey lads, he's in here!'

-

I told my psychiatrist I'm obsessed with anything to do with the moon. She said it's just a phase I'm going through.

-

Disappointed not to go through to the finals of 'Surgeon of the Year'. I didn't make the final cut.

-

Doctor: 'Mercury is in Uranus.'
Patient: 'I didn't know you were into astrology.'
Doctor: 'I'm not. I've just broken the thermometer.'

-

In the hospital, Granny's last words were, 'Will you pull the…' so I pulled the plug and she was gone… did she mean the curtains?

-

'What do we want?'
'Hearing aids!'
'When do we want them?'
'Pint of Guinness!'

-

I twisted my ankle yesterday while digging for gold. The hospital informed me it was just a miner injury.

A plastic surgeon's office is the only place where no one gets offended when you pick your nose.

-

My psychiatrist told me that I am paranoid. I wonder who else he's told?

-

I went to Alcoholics Anonymous and told them I couldn't stop gambling. The bloke there said, 'You need Gamblers Anonymous.' I said, 'You're right, I'm too drunk to know where I am!'

-

A friend of mine asked me what my plans were for the day. I said I was going to an optician to collect a pair of glasses and after that… we'll see.

-

I'm worried that my addiction to helter-skelters is spiralling out of control.

-

I remember when the optician told me I need glasses. Well, I say optician, but it could have been anyone really.

-

I'm developing a dry skin ointment. It's taking a long time as I'm starting from scratch.

-

I went to the doctors and said, 'I've been bitten by a wolf.'
He said, 'Where?'
'No just an ordinary one.'

'It's the Weak Bladder Association AGM tonight. If you can't make it, just give us a tinkle.'

-

I was on my way to an optician's appointment and guess who I bumped into? Just about everyone!

-

I've had to break up with my imaginary friend. I've started seeing someone else.

-

The doctor prescribed me some anti-gloating cream. 'How do I use it?' I asked. 'Well, you don't rub it in.'

-

I used to have a phobia that I was being followed by a clown, but now I can look back and laugh.

-

When I die, I'm donating my body to science. More specifically, a scientist who is working on bringing people back from the dead!

-

I've been diagnosed with Kleptomania. But I'm sure there's something I can take for it!

-

I was in the supermarket today when a box of toilet roll fell on me. I'm OK – just some soft tissue damage.

-

First the doctor told me the good news - I was going to have a disease named after me!

I accidentally drank a bottle of disappearing ink and now I'm in A & E waiting to be seen!

-

My friend opened a chest with a penknife… Fantastic pirate, not such a good surgeon.

-

Just bought my first ever First Aid kit. I thought I'd treat myself!

-

I told my doctor that I had Northern Irish voices coming out of my tummy. He said that I had a stomach Ulster.

-

Due to a mix up in Urology, orange juice will not be on the hospital menu today.

-

My poor knowledge of Greek mythology has always been my Achilles' kneecap.

HISTORY

Karl Marx is a historically famous figure, but nobody ever mentions his sporting sister, Onya, who invented the starting pistol.

-

I bought a suit of armour because I thought it would make me feel young and strong again. But when I put it on, I just felt middle aged!

-

I came second in a Winston Churchill look-alike competition. Close, but no cigar.

HOLIDAYS

Due to an unfortunate spacing error while booking our holiday, we are now looking forward to a week on Norfolk B roads.

-

I remember going to Blackpool for my holidays, and I rode on a donkey. It took me twenty-six days to get there.

-

I love climbing into a small suitcase... I can hardly contain myself.

HOME

My neighbour had all his grass stolen last night. He's outside now, looking forlorn.

-

I've been bored recently, so I decided to take up fencing. The neighbours keep demanding that I put it back.

-

I stood waving at my friendly neighbour for five minutes this morning, before realising she was only cleaning her windows.

-

I put up an electric fence around my house. My neighbour is dead against it.

-

When I moved into my new Igloo my friends threw me a surprise housewarming party... Now I'm homeless!

-

I scared the postman today by going to the door completely naked. I'm not sure what scared him more, my naked body, or the fact that I knew where he lived!

We've hired an Eastern European cleaner, but it took her fifteen hours to hoover the house. Turns out she was a Slovak.

-

I'm looking to buy a Lighthouse... Something quite plain, not too flashy!

-

Unfortunately my inflatable house got punctured during the last storm. I'm now living in a flat.

-

Got home and the window cleaner was shouting and swearing. I assume he must have lost his rag.

-

A bloke in a Parcelforce van stopped me in the street and asked me for the time.
I replied: 'It's between 9am and 5pm.' then walked off.

-

When I told my carpet fitter I didn't want coverings on my steps, he gave me a blank stair.

-

I'm at an auction, bidding for a house with an extended corridor. I'm in it for the long hall.

LIFE

I threw a boomerang away a couple of years ago and I now live in constant fear.

-

Just had a fight with the world's most forgetful man. I taught him a lesson he'll never remember.

-

People who use selfie sticks need to have a good, long look at themselves.

-

I can always tell if someone is lying... I can also tell if they're standing or leaning as well!

-

I wanted to go to a fancy dress party as a driving instructor, but I couldn't find the right gear.

-

I'm going to the barber's later today, then I have my band's percussion practice in the morning. I suppose you could say, 'Hair today, gong tomorrow.'

-

I'm really annoyed. I was on the verge of winning the 'World's Most Congested Nose' competition... and then I blew it!

The voices in my head may not be real, but they have some good ideas!

-

I went to a fancy dress party and ended up fighting a bloke dressed as a mop. I wiped the floor with him!

-

I've always been very lazy. I've got a smoke alarm that's got a snooze button.

-

I collect clocks, watches, hourglasses, stopwatches, even sundials... I seem to have too much time on my hands!

-

If attacked by a mob of clowns, always remember to go for the juggler!

-

I feel so strongly about graffiti in toilet cubicles that I've signed a partition.

-

I've been accused of not knowing how to shave properly. Bloody cheek!

-

I went to a fancy dress party last night dressed as a clock. It was a shame, but I had to leave early because everyone kept winding me up.

What happened when the pirate Bluebeard fell overboard in the Red Sea?
He got marooned.

-

I hosted a hide and seek party yesterday. I'm having a hard time finding a winner.

LOVE & MARRIAGE

Arguing with a woman is like being arrested. Everything you say can, and will, be used against you later… sometimes much later!

-

The scariest thing in life is when your wife says to you, 'Guess what today is?'

-

My wife called me immature. I nearly fell out of my tree house.

-

My wife said, 'You haven't heard a word I said, have you?' I was taken aback… What a weird way to start a conversation.

-

Bob and his wife started a diet two weeks ago. His wife suggested a 'cheat day.' She brought home KFC chicken wings… he brought home his secretary!
The doctors say he's in a stable condition.

-

I bought my wife a pug dog yesterday. Despite the squashed nose, the bulging eyes and the rolls of fat, the dog still likes her!

My wife said she was going to dig a hole in the garden and fill it with water. I think she means well!

-

A bloke was killed by a shark whilst on honeymoon. He didn't suffer long… he was only married ten days!

-

You can tell a lot about a woman by her hands… If they are around your throat, she is probably upset.

-

I warned my wife not to use the twelve inch long cotton buds in the bathroom. She didn't listen. It went in one ear and out the other.

-

Ten years ago, I married my best friend. My wife's still really angry, but Dave and I were drunk and thought it was funny.

-

My wife said, 'Why don't you treat me like you did when we first dated?' So I took her out to dinner, then dropped her off at her parent's house!

-

I met my wife on the net. We worked for a circus… We were both rubbish trapeze artists.

-

I'm always arguing with my wife as she is obsessed with playing Twister. I just don't know where I stand with her.

-

My wife has just left me because I'm so insecure.
No, hang on, she's back… She just went to put the bin out.

-

I asked my wife what she was burning for dinner? As it turns out, it was all my personal belongings!

-

I bought my wife a broken submarine on eBay for her birthday. That didn't go down well.

-

I asked my wife what women really want. She said, 'Attentive lovers.' Or maybe she said, 'A tent of lovers…' Something like that.

-

My wife left me because of her obsession with graffiti. Apparently, the writing was on the wall.

-

Just found out my wife married me for my art collection. She only wanted me for my Monet.

-

My wife said, 'For a change, take me somewhere popular and expensive.' So I took her to a petrol station.

-

My wife is a radiographer. I get a daily x-ray of her chest. It's a bit weird, but it shows her heart's in the right place.

-

My wife says my two major faults are that I don't listen, and something else…

My wife isn't talking to me. She said I had ruined her birthday. I'm not sure how, I didn't even know it was her birthday!

-

My wife was excited about going out for tea and biscuits. She was less happy about the pint of blood.

-

My wife left me for an electrician who promised her the earth.

-

Because of the usual last-minute rush, I'm booking a table early for Valentine's Day. I don't even know if my wife likes snooker?

-

My wife has left me due to my obsession with jigsaws. Now I suppose I will have to pick up the pieces.

-

My wife left me today, saying I put sports ahead of her... We were together for six seasons.

-

My wife forced me to go to a fancy dress party last night as an exhaust pipe... I was fuming.

-

My mate's wife has left him and taken the collection of reggae records and the satellite dish. No Woman, No Sky.

My wife threatened to leave me because of my Buddy Holly obsession. I thought, 'That'll be the day.'

-

What's the difference between a man buying a lottery ticket and arguing with his wife?
He stands a chance of winning the lottery!

-

My wife has taken everything I own, and ran off with a drainage engineer. I'm going to sewer!

-

I was so bored I swapped the wrappers on my tub of Celebrations. My wife is not happy; she got her Snickers in a Twix.

-

I discovered that you can turn your ordinary sofa into a sofa-bed, simply by forgetting your anniversary.

-

Wife: 'I have blisters on my hands from the broom!'
Husband: 'Take the car next time!'

-

I recently went to a wedding. It was very emotional. The bride and groom cried. The parents cried. Even the cake had tiers.

-

You can tell a lot about a woman by her foot… If it's travelling towards you at speed, this indicates she's upset with you!

My wife and I are moving into a tree house. I hope we never fall out.

-

Apparently I'm not the most important man in my wife's life. You wait until I find this John Lewis bloke!

-

My wife had no idea I drank until I came home sober one night.

MATES

My best mate at school was called Keth. He was missing an eye.

-

My mate was knighted for his contribution to Pottery. 'Arise, Sir Ramic.'

-

I gave my friend an apple. He told me he preferred pears, so I gave him another apple.

-

I lent a mate of mine £15K to get a facelift. I need the money back now, but I don't know what he looks like.

-

My friend told me to put all my money on a horse called 'Landfill.' The horse came last – it was a rubbish tip!

-

My mate phoned and told me he had changed his name to 'Spinal Column.' I said, 'OK, can I call you back?'

-

My mate claims that he can tighten nuts and bolts just by sitting on them. I think he's torquing out of his backside!

I met a bloke at a party who said he was a lumberjack. He was a great fella.

-

My mate fell into a display of golf clubs in a sports shop. The doctors don't think he's out of the woods yet.

-

I bought my friend an elephant for their room. He said, 'Thank you very much.' I said, 'Don't mention it.'

MILITARY

I asked my boss why I had lost my job as an interrogator, but he wouldn't tell me!

-

Sometimes you miss someone so much, it makes you question why you became a sniper in the first place.

-

The bomb disposal course I subscribe to is quite disappointing. It's mainly concerned with ticking boxes.

-

Apple is working on an electronic, all-seeing device for the Navy. It's called the EyeEye Captain.

-

I'll never forget my granddad coming home from the war with one leg. We never did find out who it belonged to.

-

I jumped in a taxi in London and said, 'Waterloo please.' The driver said, 'The station?' I replied: 'Well I'm a bit late for the battle!'

A training sergeant grumbles at his young recruit, 'I didn't see you at camouflage training this morning, Private.'

'Thank you so much, Sir.'

-

I couldn't work out why I was so tired today, but then I realised I've just finished a 31-day March!

MUSIC

'To do is to be.' – Nietzsche.
'To be is to do.' – Kant.
'Do be do be do.' – Sinatra.

-

Today was Motown weather... three degrees and four tops!

-

A coachload of jazz musicians has just broken down on the M25. Expect lengthy jams.

-

The world's greatest keyboard player was called Colourblind McGinty. He sure knew how to tickle the greens.

-

Loofahs come in four sizes: Small, medium, large and Vandross!

-

Meatloaf got married to an accountant. She'll do anything for love, but she won't do VAT.

-

My mate was in a sixties band called The Hinges. They used to support The Doors.

Just heard that Sting has mysteriously disappeared; the Police haven't got a lead.

-

Elton John just bought his pet rabbit a small treadmill... It's a little fit bunny.

-

My wife asked me to stop singing 'I'm a Believer' by the Monkees. At first I thought she was joking, but then I saw her face.

-

I'm just on my way to fix Cat Steven's tent. The awning has broken.

-

I went to see my bank manager today. I said I was in dire straits. He was really helpful, practically offering me money for nothing.

-

I've finally been invited to join the local harp playing group. But to get in I had to pull a few strings.

-

I fainted in the Indian restaurant when I heard R.E.M. had split up. That's me in the Korma!

-

I have a friend who writes music about sewing machines. He's a singer songwriter... or sew it seams!

-

I used to be obsessed with the rock band 'Free'... But I'm All Right Now.

I can't stop singing 10cc songs. I think it's just a silly phase I'm going through.

-

The USA should open a chain of Elvis Presley steakhouses. It will be for people who love meat tender.

-

I opened my fridge last night and I heard a spring onion singing a Bee Gee's song. It was just the chive talkin'.

-

The doctor told me I have a bad case of the 'Herman Hermits'… But I woke up this morning feeling fine!

-

I went to a fancy dress party as a harp. The host said, 'You're not a harp, your costume is too small!' I said, 'Are you calling me a lyre?'

-

As kids we loved playing Knock Down Ginger… but we never bothered any of the other Spice Girls!

MYSTIC

Someone stole my mood ring today. I'm not really sure how I feel about it.

-

I was lucky I went to a psychic. She told me someone was going to swindle me out of some money. Best £500 I've ever spent!

-

I went to a psychic who was wildly happy. Then I saw a clairvoyant who was grumpy... I'm just looking for a happy medium.

-

Some countries are banning the use of plastic straws. This was predicted by a 16th Century seer called 'Nostrawdamus.'

-

I was on eBay and saw a crystal ball priced quite cheaply. I thought, 'that's worth looking into.'

-

I saw a fortune teller yesterday. She said a lot of money was coming my way. Today I got run over by a Securicor van!

Just got sacked from my job as a magazine clairvoyant… I didn't see that coming!

-

Aladdin has been banned from the magic carpet race for using performance enhancing rugs.

-

I'm going to have to take my 'Signs of the Zodiac' jigsaw puzzle back to the shop. It's got Pisces missing.

-

The BBC reports a psychic dwarf has escaped from prison today… Police say there is a small medium at large.

-

I went to see the Bermuda Philharmonic Orchestra. It was really strange, the triangle player disappeared!

-

A genie granted me one wish, so I said I just wanted to be happy.
Now I'm living in a cottage with six dwarves and working in a mine!

-

I got home and there was a dead chicken flying around the house. I rang the vicar and said, 'Get here quickly I've got a poultrygeist!'

-

I almost had a psychic girlfriend… but she left me before we met!

NATURE

I threw a ball for my dog. A bit extravagant, but he looks great in a dinner jacket.

-

Well stone the crows! I'm in trouble with the RSPB again.

-

My budgie broke his leg so I splinted it with a matchstick. When he tried to walk his face lit up!

-

I wrote a story on a penguin. In retrospect, I should have used paper!

-

I just killed a massive spider crawling across the floor with my shoe. I don't care how big the spider, no one steals my shoe.

-

As a newly qualified vet, I am now able to treat animals. Last night I took a couple of goats out for drinks.

-

I keep receiving bunches of flowers with the heads cut off. I think I'm being stalked.

I was known as 'The RSPCA Whistle-blower'… Yes, it was me who let the cat out of the bag!

-

Whilst walking, a lady stopped me and asked why I had a cabbage on a lead. I thought it was a collie!

-

I bought birdseed from an online pet shop, and now they are asking for feedback.

-

I taught my dog how to fetch beer. That might not sound too impressive, until you realise he gets it from the neighbours' fridge.

-

I asked my hairdresser if she had ever given a henna rinse. 'No.' she said, but she had given a duck a bath.

-

The other day in a charity shop, I bought an old record called 'Sounds Wasps Make.' I started playing it at home and thought: 'That's not the sound of wasps,' then I realised I was playing the bee side!

-

My neighbour was crying while mowing the lawn. I asked him if he was alright. He said he was, but just going through a rough patch.

-

I was offered a £100 bet that I couldn't do a butterfly impression. I thought to myself, 'Well, that's worth a flutter.'

I've lost loads of weight just by wearing bread on my head. It's a loaf hat diet!

-

When I was young I used to walk the plank... We couldn't afford a dog.

-

My dog swallowed an old roll of camera film. I called the vet and she told me to wait and see what develops.

-

The family hated it when I put ginger in their curry. They really loved that cat!

-

I hired a landscape gardener, but he wouldn't work for me as my garden is portrait.

-

I went on holiday with my horse; it was self-cantering.

-

I popped into a garden centre in Wimbledon. I wondered if they have any top seeds?

-

I went to a safari park and got charged at by a rhino. I was shocked – ten pounds for a photo!

-

The blue whale is so big that, if it was laid on a football pitch, they would have to abandon the match.

-

I get a real kick out of training wild animals to do tricks. At the weekend the hares stood on the back of my neck.

I was advised that my dog needed to be chipped. I only had a nine iron but I still got it over the shed!

-

Pollen is what happens when flowers can't keep it in their plants!

-

Three lions on my shirt... That's the last time I'll get out of the car at Longleat.

-

I pulled a drowning fisherman out of the river yesterday, but he was a bit on the small side – so I threw him back in!

-

My brother has the heart of a lion... and a lifetime ban from Bristol Zoo.

-

Did you know you can tell the gender of an ant by throwing it in the water? If it sinks it's a girl ant, but if it floats it's buoyant.

-

A friend asked me: 'What's your pet hate?' I replied: 'He's not keen on going to the vets.'

-

I'm thinking of going into the pet business, selling various breeds of dog.
Does anyone have any pointers?

-

What has lots of legs and a machine gun? A caterkiller!

I went to the head office of the RSPCA. It's absolutely tiny - you couldn't swing a cat!

-

I was recently mauled by a herd of cows. I'm OK, I was just grazed.

-

I killed a spider with a shoe earlier… I don't know how it lost the other seven!

-

The first man to receive a pig's heart was known to his friends as upbeat, funny and full of energy. Now they say he's a bit of a boar.

PLANES, TRAINS & AUTOMOBILES

Apparently I snore so loudly that it scares everyone in the car I'm driving!

-

A man jumps into a taxi and says, 'King Arthur's Close.'
Taxi driver: 'Don't worry, we'll lose him at the next set of traffic lights!'

-

At least the Eurostar's comfortable. It's murder on the Orient Express!

-

Engineers have created a car that can run on parsley. They now want to create a train that can run on thyme.

-

Just spent four hours waxing the car… but I'm not sure how it gets so hairy?

-

I decided to splash out and buy myself something expensive today… So I filled up my car with petrol!

I used to have a speedbump phobia, but slowly I got over it.

-

Generally Americans don't like German cars, but I've heard a lot of cowboys are buying the new Audi.

-

Did you know 30% of all Swedish car accidents involve a moose? They shouldn't let them drive!

-

Unfortunately my friend was hit by a steam train. I was sad, but he was chuffed to bits.

-

Every morning I go outside and get hit by the same pushbike. I think it's a vicious cycle.

-

I always get a 147 when I play snooker. It stops right outside the hall.

-

I finally had the courage to stand up at my AA meeting and admit I had a problem... It was my starter motor.

-

I tried to invent the cold air balloon, but I gave up on the project as it never really took off!

-

I've just seen a car being driven by a sheep in a swimsuit. It was a lamb bikini.

A truck loaded with onions overturned on the M25. Motorists are advised to pull over and find a hard shoulder to cry on.

POLITICS

The CEO of IKEA has been elected as Sweden's Prime
Minister. He is expected to have a cabinet assembled by
the weekend.

-

The Welsh Assembly have launched an investigation
after confidential documents were made public. They're
blaming a leek.

ROYALTY

(Singing) 'Oh, the Grand old Duke of York, he had ten million quid, he gave it to an American girl for something 'he never did!'

SARTORIAL ELEGANCE

I bought a pair of Velcro trousers the other day, but never again. They were a total rip-off.

-

I used to hate facial hair… but then it grew on me.

-

I bought some tortoiseshell patterned shoes the other day. They are really nice, but it took me three hours to leave the shop.

-

The barber asked, 'Short back and sides?'
'No… long legs!'

-

Two silkworms decided to have a race. It ended in a tie!

-

I've just bought myself a new reversible jacket. I'm really excited to see how it turns out.

-

Yesterday, I waited in all day for a tailor to come round and shorten my trousers. Will he turn up?

I asked my barber, 'What cut would make me look handsome?'

'A power cut!'

-

People have been making remarks about me choosing to wear mittens rather than gloves – but I'm not going to point fingers.

'SHAKING SHEETS'

I always cry after sex... 500 quid is a lot of money!

-

Just bought Cluedo: Swingers Edition. Turns out they all did it... in every room!

-

You can now get Viagra in tea bags. It doesn't make you better in bed, it just keeps your dunked biscuits from going soft!

-

The wife wants me to do page seven of the Kama Sutra, but I don't. It puts me in an awkward position.

-

My mates bet me a hundred quid that I couldn't take five Viagra tablets at once. But I thought, 'How hard can it be?'

-

I've just discovered an origami porn site but, its paper view.

-

I don't like to use double-entendres... but occasionally I'll slip one in!

I've been taking Viagra for my sunburn. It doesn't cure it, but at night it does keep the sheets off my legs!

-

How do you spot a blind man at a nudist camp? It's not hard.

-

My mate went to see a psychic last week, who told him he would be coming into money. Strangely enough, he spent last night with a woman called Penny!

-

I asked my wife to stimulate me with a keyring, but she just kept fobbing me off!

-

I received a letter inviting me to try the local nudist club at the weekend. I thought, 'Why not, I haven't anything on!'

-

I went to the library for a book on men who aren't well-endowed. The librarian said, 'It's not in yet.' I said, 'That's the one I need!'

-

We've just found out my mate is addicted to Viagra. His girlfriend is taking it very hard.

-

I went for a massage, but it wasn't great, so I only gave a one-star review. I guess I was just rubbed up the wrong way.

I was sitting on the bus today, and next to me was a beautiful young lady reading a book: 'Strange but true sexual facts.'

'Is it interesting?' I asked. 'Yes, it is,' she replied. 'Did you know that Native Americans have the longest penis in the world, while the Irish have the thickest. Oh I am sorry, my name is Helen, what's yours?'

'Tonto O'Riley!'

-

I'm a big fan of pepper, so I made a bid on eBay for a grinder. I'm off now to meet a man who says he has a 'twelve-incher' to show me.

SPORT

I've got some racing geese for sale. Let me know if you want a quick gander.

-

Storm warning:
Footballers: 'Don't travel unless necessary.'
Rugby players: 'Training as normal.'

-

A hippo can run and swim faster than a person, so cycling is the only chance of beating it in a triathlon.

-

It takes a lot of balls to golf the way I do.

-

I went to the doctors and he told me I needed a pacemaker... Now I have a Kenyan athlete two metres ahead of me everywhere I go!

-

My wife asked me if I had seen the dog bowl. To be honest, I didn't know he played cricket.

-

I went to watch drag racing the other day. I was impressed at how fast they can run in high heels.

I don't watch football... If I wanted to see grown men struggle to score in ninety minutes, I'd go to a bar.

-

I was going to organise a blindfold marathon, but I thought, 'Where do I start?'

-

Our local cricket club is looking for a wicket-keeper, on a salary of 10K a week.
There's got to be a catch.

-

I think I want to take up acting... What's the name of the local football team?

-

Last night, I dreamt someone was saying, 'On your marks... Get Set... Go!' I woke up with a start!

SOCIAL MEDIA

At breakfast, my wife said she's leaving me because of my obsession with Twitter. I nearly choked on my #brown!

STAGE & SCREEN

Welcome to 'OCD, The Musical.' Starring, in order of height...

-

I told my actor friend to break a leg. 'Why?' he said. 'You're in a cast.'

-

Talking of actors...I recently met 'The Rock' who was actually quite shy. I thought he would be a little bolder!

-

I went into my local butchers and asked him for some tripe. He gave me a Love Island box set.

-

Due to my obsession with TV detectives, my wife suggested we split up. I thought, 'Great'... we can cover more ground!'

-

I said, 'I'm going to buy a theatre.' My wife said, 'Are you having me on?'
'Well I'll give you an audition but I can't promise.'

-

I was very disappointed when I saw Dunkirk. I expected William Shatner's autobiography.

Just watched a film about a killer teabag. I was surprised that it was only given a PG rating.

-

My friend's daughter has just got a part in the stage musical 'Cats.' She should be able to put a lot in the kitty.

-

The theatre sacked me as their stage designer. I left without making a scene.

-

Does anybody know if the film, 'The River Wild,' is available for streaming?

-

I thought Tom Cruise was a boating holiday for male cats.

-

The BBC are considering a new reality show based on imprisoned airline employees. The pilot is out next week.

-

I had a bet on Hans Solo to win 'Best Star Wars Character.' Well, he was the Wookie's favourite!

-

I was asked to dress up as Matt Damon's secret agent character. People must think I was Bourne yesterday.

-

My ventriloquist act is fantastic… even though I say it myself!

I'm upset that I missed the hairdressing championship on TV. I wonder if there will be highlights?

-

Have you noticed, on the BBC evening news they always begin with 'Good evening.' and then proceed to tell you why it isn't.

TECH

I bought a 'smart' light switch, but it was much too clever for me. So I swapped it for a dimmer switch.

-

I asked my mate why he was talking into an envelope. He said he was sending a voicemail!

-

I can't see an end! I have no control! No home, and there's really no escape... I really must buy a new keyboard.

-

3D printers are so realistic now. I produced a life-size Bob Marley playing the guitar and the printer started 'jammin'.'

-

Apparently you aren't allowed to use 'beef stew' as a password online – it's not stroganoff.

THE GREAT 'PAUSE' (COVID)

LOCKDOWN 1

I decided to finish off various things I had started at home... So I finished off a bottle of Merlot, then a bottle of Chardonnay, then a boggle of wum, then whistty, then... then... zzzz.

-

They said a mask and gloves were enough to go to the supermarket. They lied, everybody else had clothes on!

-

I suffered an unpleasant side effect after my second Covid vaccine... I was told to go back into the office!

-

From Monday, postmen will be working from home. They will read your letters and ring you if it's anything important.

-

Just asked the wife to put on her nurse's uniform. 'Why? Are you feeling horny?' She asked.
'No, we just need some more milk!'

-

I thought PPI was something you got if you didn't wear goggles in a swimming pool!

Day 2 without sports:
Found a lady sitting on my couch. Apparently she's my wife… She seems nice.

-

Covid Warning: People must not cough near you; they must cough far away.
If they cough near you can tell them to FAR COUGH!

-

If you get an email that has 'Knock, knock.' in the subject line, don't open it as it's just a Jehovah's Witness working from home!

-

Seen at Dollis Hill Underground Service Information:
Thought for the day:
If anyone is going to make a facemask out of an old bra, make sure you use the left cup. After all, you don't want to go out looking like a right tit!

VILLAINY

I must be the worst hangman ever. I've let everybody down.

-

I ordered a book called 'How to Scam People Online.' It's been months and it still hasn't arrived!

-

An ice cream van has caught fire on the M25. Police are currently putting out the cones.

-

I think my neighbour is a serial killer and I am going to ring the police... as soon as he finishes laying my patio!

-

When I was a kid, my mum said I could be anyone I wanted to be. Turns out the police class this as 'identity fraud.'

-

A ventriloquist was murdered by his own doll, but the police decided it was suicide, as he must have had a hand in it.

-

I bought myself a memory foam mattress. Now it's trying to blackmail me.

A warning to the man who stole my owl costume. I'd be looking over my shoulder if I were you.

-

Airport police say people smuggling helium in their luggage are under control, but cases will continue to rise.

-

I bought a pair of trainers from a drug dealer. I don't know what they were laced with, but I kept on tripping.

-

I got stopped by the police last night who asked me, 'Where were you between six and eight?'
'Junior School.'

-

Last night I got tasered by a policewoman. I found her stunning.

-

Always have a positive outlook on life... unless you're being breathalysed.

-

The police rang me to say they had recovered my stolen sofa. That was nice of them... it was starting to look a bit tatty.

-

A policeman stopped me whilst driving and told me I had a flat tyre. Luckily, I had a foot pump in the boot. So I knocked him out with it and drove off!

To the person who stole my train set: What goes around, comes around...

-

Police have confirmed the man who died after falling off the roof of a nightclub was not a bouncer.

-

I got arrested for stealing a copy of Trivial Pursuit. Now I've got some tricky questions to answer!

-

Local police hunting the 'Knitting Needle Nutter,' who has stabbed six people in the backside in the last forty-eight hours, believe the attacker could be following some kind of pattern.

-

I woke up this morning and found a policewoman in my bed. She assured me it was OK as she was working undercover.

-

My mate was recently arrested for stealing a garden clothes rotary airer. He got away with it as his lawyers said it wouldn't stand up in court.

-

The police came round and accused me of stealing a chicken. I had to make a run for it.

-

I got home and a burglar was pressing one of my shirts. So I punched him, as you have to strike while the iron's hot.

I've been sentenced to twenty years for my part in a timeshare fraud. Luckily, I only have to go to prison for two weeks every year.

-

I was interrogated by a pair of farmers. Good crop, bad crop.

-

In the news, a shop assistant fought off a robber with a label gun. Police are looking for a man with a price on his head.

WHEELING AND DEALING

I was an accountant from the age of twenty to thirty and then I was sacked for no reason. What a waste of fourteen years.

-

I have just started a business selling home surgery kits, called 'Suture Self.'

-

Did you know that a shoal of piranhas can strip a body to the bone in thirty seconds? Anyway, I've lost my job at the Aquatic Centre.

-

A bloke at work denies taking the batteries out of my calculator… but it just doesn't add up!

-

Just got a job as an executioner at the Tower of London. I've got my train ticket and will beheading there later.

-

My friend has just started a new job on a farm, helping out with birthing goats. I thought, 'You must be kidding.'

There's nothing better than sitting beside a roaring fire, spiced wine in hand, singing carols. Maybe that's why I am no longer a firefighter.

-

I've got a job with a one-armed typist to help with capital letters. It's shift work.

-

I got a job in a perfume factory, but I was soon scent packing.

-

I once worked as a cinema usher... I was in a dark place back then.

-

Being part of the 'Dream Team' was my downfall. I got sacked for sleeping on the job!

-

Job interview question:
'Can you perform under pressure?'
'No, but I'll give 'Bohemian Rhapsody' a go!'

-

I lost my job at the bank on my first day. A woman asked me to check her balance... so I pushed her over!

-

My mate got a job at a furniture manufacturer. One day he fell into an upholstery machine, but he's fully recovered.

-

My boss is going to fire the employee with the worst posture. I have a hunch it might be me.

There was a tap on the door this morning. I do wish the plumber would start paying attention to what he's doing!

-

A large oil company is going to start producing fuel from flying insect urine. It's BP.

-

It's possible to open a new hairdressing salon, but only if you cut your costs, and crimp and save.

-

I've got a part-time job drawing margins on paper. It's an interesting side line.

-

I went for a job interview and the manager said, 'We are looking for someone who is responsible.'
'Well, I'm your man,' I replied. 'In my last job, whenever anything went wrong, they said I was responsible.'

-

My grave-digger friend is off work sick, so I have offered to fill in for him.

-

I'm so bored at my job at the Ice Cream Museum. I just sit there all day staring at Walls.

-

I'm working on a factory line making toy Dracula dolls. There are only two of us, so I have to make every second count.

I have just been offered a job making Blackpool rock. After all, how hard can it be?

-

My uncle used to manufacture clown shoes. It was no small feet.

-

I've just been offered a job interview with a North African fruit company. I'm waiting for them to come back with a few dates.

-

I packed up my job at the camera factory. They were too negative and didn't develop my career.

-

A mate of mine was trying to get a job as a Lexicographer, so I put a good word in for him.

-

I paused the film last night and went and made a cup of coffee. Perhaps that is why I am no longer a film projectionist.

-

I used to work for a scuba diving training company, but unfortunately it went under.

-

I got sacked last week for not hitting my targets. I guess I wasn't meant to be an archery instructor.

I'm working at an ammunition factory. I must be doing OK as I think I'm up for an award. Rumour has it I'm getting the bullet.

-

Poundstretcher and Marks and Spencer are to merge. I'm not convinced the new name 'Stretch Marks' is the best idea.

-

I couldn't stand my job at the clock factory. They were so rude… Everyone kept making faces!

-

I had to quit my job at the watch factory. Now I seem to have plenty of time on my hands.

-

I recently went for a job interview as a bin man. I asked if there was any training. They said, 'You just pick it up as you go along.'

-

I want to install a suggestion box at work… Does anyone know how to do it?

-

It really annoys me when people phone me to complain about the terrible weather. This may be why I lost my job in Mountain Rescue.

-

I've just heard that Victoria's Secret and Smith and Wesson are merging. The new name will be: TittyTittyBangBang.

I bought a fan in the sales. It was so cheap... I was blown away.

-

My fresh herb business was failing so badly, the bank had to call in the bayleafs.

-

The calendar factory dismissed me for poor performance. I should have seen my days were numbered.

-

The recession is really starting to hit my fart joke business. I used to have three people working for me, but I've just let one go.

-

I've had to give up my job as a contortionist. I just couldn't make ends meet!

-

I've been sacked from my job on the synchronised fireworks display team. Apparently I was a bang out of order.

-

I've just invented the first thought-controlled air-freshener. If you think about it... it just makes scents!

-

I was dismissed from my job at the tape measure factory. Apparently it was because I kept breaking the rules.

My dad used to say: 'Many hands make light work.' Mind you, he managed a team of five, repairing street lamps.

The Naked Story:
Fiction about Fiction

A Concise Guide to Metafiction

Jason Bellipanni, M.A., M.F.A.

Sent From the Past Publishers
Published by Story Review Press
4 Grand Hill Rd, #504, Mont Vernon, NH 03057 USA
Story Review Press, Registered Offices: 107 N. Main Street, Concord, NH 03301-4989

This is a work of fiction. Names, characters, places, and incidents either are the product of the author's imagination or are used fictitiously, and any resemblance to actual persons, living or dead, business establishments, events, or locales is entirely coincidental.

While the author has made every effort to provide accurate telephone numbers and internet addresses at the time of publication, neither the publisher nor the author assumes responsibility for errors, or for changes that occur after publication. Further, publisher does not have any control over and does not assume responsibility for author or thord-party websites or their content.

The Last Elf-Mite was first published in Feathers and Cigarettes: An Anthology, Fish Publishing, Ireland, 2003. *Dust* was first published in The Berkeley Fiction Review, University of California, Berkeley, 2000. *Skin and Rain* was published in BLINK: Flash Fiction Anthology, The Paper Journey Press, 2006

First Story Press Review trade paperback edition: January 2013
PRINT. TRADE. PAPERBACK. ISBN- **ISBN-13: 978-1939644060**
Library of Congress Cataloging-in-Publication Data

Bellipanni, Jason (1971-)
        The Naked Story: Fiction about Fiction. A Concise Guide
        to Metafiction / by Jason Bellipanni
        p.286
        ISBN **1939644062** 1The Naked Story: Fiction about Fiction.
        A Concise Guideto Metafiction

PRINTED IN THE UNITED STATES OF AMERICA

CONTENTS

Praise for Jason Bellipanni "I found Jason Bellipanni's protagonist in 'Skin and Rain' to be one of the most compelling characters I've come across recently." *Wanda Wade Mukherjee, Editor, Paper Journey Press. From the Introduction to Blink.*

"Jason is one of the most talented writers I have worked with; his facility with language and his ability to maintain tension within an intergenerational narrative betray his intelligence, diligence, and artistic vision." *Lewis Robinson, author of Officer Friendly: Stories and Water Dogs*

"*The Last Elf-Mite* most definitely did surprise me, like some skewed but ordinary Harold Pinter domestic episode eccentrically reworked by Isaac Asimov. I found it courageous and fastidious and unflinching in its courage. A writer well worth watching, I feel." *Pat McCabe, author of the Booker nominated novels The Dead School, and The Butcher Boy. From the Introduction to Feathers and Cigarettes*

"As Editor-in-Chief of *The Cream City Review*, I read hundreds of submissions by emerging and established fiction writers each year and I can tell you with absolute certainty that Jason's work is not only refreshing and cutting edge, it's topnotch and represents some of the best new writing I've seen. He's a writer to watch." *Karen Auvinen, poet, winner of an Academy of American Poets Award.*

"His composition textbook is fascinating, strikingly original yet educationally effective. He not only discusses classic composition textbook subjects—description, narration, the brainstorming process, persuasion, research, etc.—but dares to include his own writing: vivid, detailed short stories and essays that serve as examples of different tasks and of excellent prose." *Dr. Ann Norton, English Chair, St. Anselm College*

Introduction

Greetings, Dear Reader, and welcome to "Metafiction and the Imagination Consciousness." No matter where you are, standing in a bookstore, sitting on your living room sofa, or waiting on line in a prison library, the title may cause your brain-bone to signal your finger-bone to turn the page and tell your eye-bone to find something else to read. This is your privilege, being the reader, and even though I have no real control over the context in which you've come across this essay (while hiding from the police in a dumpster, while looking through boxes of someone's unpublished material, or while flying your car on your way to excavate a section of 'old earth') I will attempt to perform a moment of lingua-scripto hypnosis on you. YAWN. Every five minutes after you've turned this page in search of something 'better' or 'more interesting' you will be reminded of this essay by a YAWN, an uncontrollable urge to YAWN. Even now, you can feel those muscles at the back of your throat—oh, how they long to be stretched. The YAWN will make you think of this essay; you will not cease to YAWN until you've returned here to do your doody. Duty.

Now then, with my evil plot afoot, we'll move on to the provocative title. You are correct to observe that the words of the title attempt to coin a new literary term— 'imagination consciousness'— by pairing it with the real, but equally unlikely word, 'Metafiction'. The success of a new term depends on its musicality as language and its immediate (usually false) sense of familiarity. The 'imagination consciousness' sounds like an idea we should have studied at one time.

Well here's another slavish devotee of the imagination, you may be thinking, which is probably about right. Nonetheless if you do not make yourself more comfortable before you begin to read this, your irritation is bound to increase and both of us will suffer in the long run. Probably both of us will suffer in the long run anyway as this seems to be a regular condition of being human and alive. But of course, I meant suffering in the administrative or academic sense. A new cup of hot tea or coffee might be just the thing right now, a little booster before you must train your eyes and your concentration on this attempt at intellectual bravado. Perhaps a cookie or two, splurge a little.

It seems that an essay of this sort can take one of two (or possibly many more) approaches. The author might dig up a familiar and well-worn literary text or author, and through a process of cutting and pasting, slap together an analysis that does nothing more than re-present some variation of a theory that has been done many times before. The inherent value in this approach is similar to the rules governing a successful new literary term; that is, the essay will touch those keys inside your mind which have been touched before, thus bringing familiarity to the surface and no doubt, some relief on your part. After all, communicating is difficult enough and we are right to embrace those ideas or theories which we've heard and dissected before; familiarity can very easily stand in for comprehension, and no doubt there are many masters who have recognized this truth.

Another approach would be to attempt to introduce, explain, and illustrate an idea that has never before been addressed or exposed. The danger here is painfully obvious—lose the reader's attention by plunging the reader into a multi-dimensional maze of interpretations and retractions, and the master of fine art risks devolving back into a Slave of Fine Arts, particularly of creative writing (SOFAPOCW).

The dilemma of whether to revive the old or blunder into the new is an ancient one. Take the first approach and it will be much easier to provoke, through an eloquent manipulation of well used critical language, the glow of familiarity that often substitutes for thought. The second approach affords no such cloak and it requires the intestinal fortitude (guts) to fail out loud, as it were, in front of God and everyone, and to forever be branded as the one who 'doesn't seem to understand much of anything.' If you sense that I am attempting to make a case for the more dangerous approach, that I am trying to bring to the surface the inherent virtue in wrestling with the more impressive beast, you are correct.

At this point, if this were a car show in Detroit, I would step up to center stage where a silky red cloth has been draped over a monstrous contraption. The lights would dim throughout the conference center, perhaps throughout the land, except for the spotlight shining on the spot where I stand, next to the hidden machine; people's conversations would quickly dry up and cease. All eyes focus on me and the dreamy sleek sex-rod that must be under such a shiny and smooth cloth. With one hand posed in a gesture of presentation and the other one gripping a handful of fabric, I yank it away like a cape and reveal another giant drapery, a cream colored silk sheet with giant red letters that continues to hide the mechanism beneath. A quiet gasp moves like a snake from mouth to mouth and I gaze upon the enormous shiny red words that appear on this sleek white cloth.

Metafiction and the Imagination Consciousness

The process of the narrative has always privileged one method of communicating and comprehending human experience over any other. Telling stories has been part of human culture, we are told, from the very beginning. It would not be surprising therefore to understand the narrative as one of the primary ways in which people have sought to organize and understand themselves. As John Gardner suggests in The Art of Fiction, "Human beings can hardly move without models for their behavior, and from the beginning of time, in all probability, we have known no greater purveyor of models than story-telling" (86).

One might even suggest that the narrative has been the most comfortable way of deriving meaning from our actions and those of others; as we grew familiar with the elements inherent in narrative we began to be able to assume and expect. We categorized personalities and searched out characteristics in order to praise the heroes and condemn the villains. We attached our minds to the increasing tension and suspense, waiting for the climax, the resolution, the moral. This method of storytelling helped ground our own consciousness. Narration made those boxes available into which we funneled our own personal experiences as well as the information to which we were exposed. Fiction writers have, for a long while, been creating box after box, attempting to fill it with new and exciting things.

Metafiction challenges those narrative components by highlighting the concept of process over the idea of product. Specifically, metafiction seeks to expose the mechanisms of the narrative: the reader's expectations, character development, plot structure, the form and language used to deliver a story, and finally the writer's role as creator. By exposing the ways in which these elements worked and the intent with which they were used in the past, metafiction accomplishes much more than an investigation of the craft or writing. By exploring how and why a story is made, Metafiction helps to reveal the way in which reality is made, the constructions of everyday life such as the role of the father or the rules governing the worker/employer relationship. The consequences of metafiction expand beyond literature and directly into the way in which we process and comprehend human experience.

Metafiction has problematized the inherent value which was once assigned to the notion of fact and calls into question any conventional understanding of a separate and objective reality. In her book Metafiction, Patricia Waugh details one of the main impacts that metafiction has had on the world outside the pages of a book:
…for metafictional writers the most fundamental assumption is that composing a novel is basically no different than composing or constructing one's 'reality'. Writing itself rather than consciousness becomes the main object of attention. Questioning not only the notion of the novelist as God, through the flaunting of the author's godlike role, but also the authority of consciousness, of the mind, metafiction established the categorization of the world through the arbitrary system of language. (Waugh 43)

This emphasis on the process of construction, through the unstable system of language, serves to upset the very idea that there can be a clear separation between fact and fiction. Communication and comprehension rely on too many variables and versions of perception to be categorized purely as one or the other; the truth, it seems,

comes from a perpetual blend of both the factual and the fictive. In this context, the function of the imagination becomes clear; this state of mind and the processes contained within are particularly suited for precisely this task of separating concepts or ideas and combining disparate elements into a meaningful whole.

In his essay entitled, "Visibility," Italo Calvino discusses the multiple characteristics of the imagination:

> ...although science interests me just because of its efforts to escape from anthropomorphic knowledge, I am nonetheless convinced that our imagination cannot be anything but anthropomorphic...But at the same time, I have always sought out in the imagination a means to attain knowledge that is outside of the individual, outside the subjective. It is right, then, for me to declare myself closer to the second position, that of (imagination as) identification with the world soul. (Memos 90-91)

The focus shift from the outcome to the process has led to destabilization in many arenas of human discourse. It has become virtually impossible to know if what we read or see is true or fictive, or both at once, and bit by bit the distinction is losing relevance. If I tell you that I heard or that I read somewhere, in some magazine, maybe Time or Newsweek that thirty eight percent of all fifteen year-olds in America regularly smoke marijuana, what is your response? Do you immediately sit down at your computer and look up the facts to establish the veracity? Or instead do you check the information against your own perceptions, your own beliefs, and the bits about the topic that you've heard or read or seen or experienced? And maybe the next time you find yourself in a conversation about drugs and teenagers you offer this bit of speculative information, since perhaps it seems reasonable enough to you.

The process, or the burden of decoding the overwhelming amount of information that we are exposed to each day has begun to shift squarely onto the individual whose effort or lack thereof determines what is believable and what is impossible.

The imagination is being called into service more and more often as individuals wade through the waves of information, make their own distinctions and develop their own personal meaning. Understanding the ways in which metafiction has shaped the act and consequences of storytelling will help identify those ways in which many people through their imagination consciousness have begun decoding and assembling their life experience and establishing their own worth and value and truth in the face of the deterioration, universally speaking, of those very same values.

Metafiction began as a critique of the assumptions and expectations that traditionally accompanied the process of narration. By first drawing attention to the gap between the created artifact and reality and ultimately confusing the two into, for example, the genre known as creative non-fiction or in some cases, journalism, Metafiction began to highlight the implicit biases and ideologies inherent in the Realist's approach.

Any text that draws the reader's attention to its process of construction by frustrating his or her conventional expectations of meaning and closure problematizes more or less explicitly the ways in which narrative codes—whether 'literary' or 'social'—artificially construct apparently 'real' and imaginary worlds in the terms of particular ideologies while presenting these as transparently 'natural' and 'eternal'. (Waugh 40)

If Metafiction could expose the inner working of fiction and reveal that the Wizard of Oz author was merely a human being with a particular set of desires and sensibilities and filters, then who was supposedly providing us with the true history, the true statistics, the true scientific theories? What if the earth really wasn't the center of the universe?

Because of the crossover success of the idea of constructing reality, the techniques of metafiction have grown out of their place as a side-show cultural experiment over the past thirty years and into mainstream culture. The genre of creative non-fiction is not the only popular medium to have adopted many of the techniques; the so-called reality television shows mimic metafiction in their elaborate and self-conscious constructions of what is then self-reflexively presented as spontaneous reality.

The techniques of metafiction, which have been liberally adopted by these genres and others, serve to remind the reader that our reality is a construction, born from the accomplishments and failures of our own imagination and that much, if not all, of the meaning of our experience as human beings is based exclusively in our mind. Metafiction breaks down the narrative model which relied on the differentiation between fact and fiction. The narrative model, because it seeks to use fiction to show the real and uses the real to create fiction, was also absolutely invested in the idea of truth versus imaginary. Without at least a cursory belief in this distinction the narrative process of comprehending our experience would not have been so popular or so comfortable. It was important to the success of each, fact and fiction, to be able at anytime to identify the difference, to ultimately separate the two. Form is just one example of the impulse to solidify the distinction: a newspaper article did not look the same as a short story.

The process of narrative itself did not distinguish between the two; history was told using the narrative model, as was myth and fable. It was important therefore that there be a supreme authority or some sort of objective reality that could perform the task of sorting one from the other.

As the establishments of authority continue to lose their credibility the burden of distinction (between fact and fiction) shifts to the individual. Jack Shafer, a journalist for Slate magazine on line explained the recent troubles that surfaced at the *New York* Times by giving the names of other journalists who were caught lying: "Last week, *New York Times* reporter Jayson Blair joined Janet Cooke, formerly of the *Washington Post,* the *New Republic's* Stephen Glass, the *Boston Globe's* Patricia Smith and Jay Forman in *Slate* as journalists who got caught embellishing, exaggerating, and outright lying in print." Blair wrote and published several entirely fictitious or partially plagiarized stories which forced the readers to recognize the humans behind the creation and communication of the 'news.'

Dan Rather of CBS delivered a story about President Bush's questionable behavior in the national guard service in the 1970's based on documents that were later proven to be forged. In one of the most blatant metafictional moments on national television, Dan Rather interviewed the secretary Marian Carr Knox about the documents; she confirmed that the documents were not authentic while offering that the sentiments behind them were probably accurate (CBSNEWS). A current national obsession with the concept of bias in the various news media organizations is even further proof that more than ever before, people are aware of the inner workings of these once trusted institutions.

The issue of fiction or non-fiction increasingly loses relevance with respect to the idea of meaning, and the ideas of the truth and fact are on their way to becoming archaic expressions precisely because they belong to a pretense or set of assumptions that have ceased to be relevant. This is not to say that fact does not exist, but it must descend from the pedestal and enter the mix on the same level as fiction. The focus on process instead of a product has led to the understanding of experience as a fluid concept in which both fact and fiction are incorporated to construct relevant meanings.

Patricia Waugh discusses the fate of reality in the face of metafictional destabilization:

"Metafiction functions through the problematization rather than the destruction of the term 'reality'. It depends on the regular construction and subversion of rules and systems. Such novels usually set up an nternally consistent 'play' world which ensures the reader's absorption, and then lays bare its rules in order to investigate the relation of fiction to reality, the concept of pretence." (Waugh 65)

In this destabilized space potential re-emerges. The roles that have been created and the relationships that have been defined and ingrained become elasticized. Male professors can wear earrings and women can commit murder; we are prevented from falling so quickly back on the boxes that have been prepared for our experiences. We hesitate. Italo Calvino confirms the imagination's ability to move and operate in this newly realized space of potential:
Still there is another definition in which I recognize myself fully, and that is the imagination as repertory of what is potential, what is hypothetical, of what does not exist and has never existed, and perhaps will never exist but might have existed…."The imagination is a kind of electronic machine that takes into account of all possible combinations and chooses the ones that are appropriate to a particular purpose, or are simply the most interesting, pleasing, or amusing" (Memos 91).

In this space, the context of what something means shakes off some of the baggage of the past, since the 'history', always presented as a story, continues to become as suspect as the term 'reality'. This is not to claim that there ceases to be value in the story of our past, but to suggest that the meaning we extract has less to do with the belief in the 'truth of occurrence' and more to do with interpretive or associative value. Do most Americans believe that President Bush may have expected preferential treatment during the dangerous Vietnam war as a national guard officer and as the son of one of the most politically connected men in America? Yes. Do the documents prove this to be true? No they do not.

Metafiction has unlocked a mode of perception, comprehension, and communication based not on a historical formula and not on the distinction between real and fake, but on the ability of our own imagination consciousness to perceive, develop, and assign meaning to our experience. The title of the paper could just as easily have been, "Imagination consciousness—the Process of Understanding Processes."

Just as narration was eventually recognized to be couched inside the logical thought process of plot and character development, metafiction has emerged from within what can now be called the imagination consciousness. This process presents techniques which have increasingly become the primary tools by which we understand our experiences. At one time the division between the true and the make-believe was the core of our comprehension of experience; the institutions and the analytical mind divided our perceptions into the true stories and the fictional, fantasy versus reality. As the amount of information, both credible and incredible continues to increase and the obvious credibility of the gate-keeping institutions continues to erode, the ability to make that division becomes increasingly problematic. The collision of the two can be easily seen in the explosion of the creative non-fiction genre, in which a single narrator assumes the ultimate authority and describes often in impossible detail the events of his or her own life—the reliance on the process of memory is the most obvious evidence of the work being done by the imagination.

In order to examine the characteristics of the imagination consciousness it's necessary to explore the process by which metafiction has transformed the narrative experience.

Metafiction's interaction with the reader as well as with the writer, its effects on character and plot, and the characteristic way all of these techniques have destabilized the boundary between fiction and reality have resulted in the illumination of this alternative perceptual apparatus that I refer to as the imagination consciousness.

At the Detroit car show, the cream-colored sheet with red lettering hovers for a moment in the air, after I've pulled it up and away. It descends slowly, like a deflating parachute with twisted red letters and finally reveals a velvet purple cloth covering a table. The crowd remains silent. Someone near the back clears their throat.

The Black Madonna Miracle

No sound. The opening scene is usually nothing but the endless expanse of dark water. Clearly the rich green and black sway of a deep ocean; the eye focuses on a hesitant white-lipped crest when it briefly appears before dispersing back into the endless push and shove. But unlike a camera lens that endlessly adjusts and re-adjusts, struggling to identify and focus and lock-in on some thing, the eyes quickly tire and settle on the wider view.

The sloshing, rocking rhythm hypnotizes the conscious mind until, growing weary of perceiving even this general ocean blur, the halt happens. The ocean's movement slows and slows until the image freezes into a giant oil painting. The flicks of a brush that tricked the eyes are exposed, and all at once, motion is as impossible here as it is on a canvas, as irretrievable as the artist's own memory of the moment. Your own existence, the reality of being alive and strapped to a balloon basket, holds its breath, turning you and your experience into art.

There is a tightening, a suffocation of sorts, when you become part of this suspended animation. To not die, to avoid becoming so much dried oil paint on a two dimensional square requires movement, a powerful push, but you cannot find purchase anywhere and you spin noiselessly, like a car tire rotating silently in an icy rut, only

an insistent rocking that gathers power will be able to rock
the self out of this rut, but you are fixed tight in place,
unable to move even your head. Nothing to do but wait
and make believe that expectation or will or mercy will
transform the art back into life.

Trapped. Dead. Or at least dying, you face the
timeless spread of quiet ocean, and your panicking mind
casts out and reels in, again and again, snagging nothing.
When the mind cannot catch, when no grappling hook
shoots out of you to wrap around something, anything, the
hungry mind does not react as the eyes have, it does not
enter peacefully into a petrified state of surrender. Instead,
the human mind turns on itself. Whirring like a dying
computer, searching and researching, the mind scrapes for
the tiniest bit of data to process. This deprivation causes
the mind to move into the water itself, and to keep itself
stimulated, it begins to strip an ocean of life and churn out
images of rusted spears, rotting nets and bloated corpses.

Not unlike the dancing silver fish at the bottom of a
green mesh net, tugging and flipping and trying to propel
itself toward the water's surface, the mind wriggles and
spasms and strains toward knowing. Creating and
delivering questions to a consciousness nearly out of power.
When is this ocean view? Noah's flood? Aemilia Earhart?
The search for John junior?

When the view pulls up and out of the water desert,
a distant coastline appears, and the shock is near electric.
The human brain gains some traction and begins processing
data. At first, it is the data of absence, a quick analysis of
what is not in evidence. No metropolitan city looms, no
sea-port with blue-gray aircraft carriers or fleets of tall-ships.
Only a beautiful coast of red and adobe-colored rock and
green hills along the horizon. All of it, dominated by an
enormous rock headland jutting out into the sea.

Inland, the rock flows into the green hills of farmland like a neck into a shoulder, and the enormous head rises one thousand feet into the air. At this point, the only dwellings exist on top of the rock; the remains of a castle wall, four or five smaller building, all of it left over from the Romans, and all of it abandoned and in decay. The Rock itself has many mythological interpretations, but at this point, it is the petrified head of an ancient beast, an octopus, said to have been turned to stone by Perseus who was using Medusa's head as a weapon in the time before he decides to give it to Athena to put on her shield.

None of this matters nearly as much as the jagged rock tentacles which are said to stretch far out underwater where they wait for the unsuspecting sailing vessel.

Finally, some sound rises up from the ocean like fog. The occasional slap of the water asserts itself above the gentle rush, the slosh of tranquility.

A ship enters into view. Thankfully there is nothing modern about this boat, nothing smacking of Disney or computer animation. Too small for Noah, too unspectacular for general audiences. This wooden ship does not fly the black skull and crossbones flag, but a brightly colored, though not altogether rectangular, red flag featuring two yellow, blurry creatures. Familiar, but not finished, either a first draft or else the results of a younger brother, trying hard to appear official and legitimate and part of the bigger picture.

This sudden ship appearance relieves the rest of the tension that develops inside the sensory deprived human mind. If the mind is an information gathering machine, hardware meant to process data, then the movement of the boat, and of the figures on the boat, provides an anchor, a fixed (though moving) point of reference; somewhere for the viewer to place their squirming attention and escape the discomforts that gather like vapors inside the mind.

The sudden close-up of the ship's deck begins to inform the viewer, begins to provide details and substance around which the limitless threads of conscious and unconscious babble begin to spin. Water-stained sails and pink-faced Scandinavian men working on the rough dark-wood stage. They carry buckets or climb rope ladders or repair the floor. Some wear tight fabric swatches on their heads, and their exposed arm and back muscles assert themselves as the men labor through the scene. The shine on their taught skin flashes under the sun and creates brief peripheral movements that mimic the occasional rodent in the shadows.

The sky darkens. One man stands tall at the helm and stares ahead, his blond hair tied in a pony-tail, his face as defined as sculpture. His icy-blue eyes seem at once to scour the immediate landscape and stare it down. A sinister expression rests comfortably on his face.

This is Count Roger, commander of this ship, and the younger brother of King Edmond the Norman. His aggressive stance makes clear his displeasure with his inferior younger brother status; Count versus King. His internal rage causes his thick fingers to twitch on the hilt of his sword and boiling jealousy occasionally clouds over his eyes.

A short and bald older man stands a good distance behind Count Roger and his lips move. His face appears wise and good, a trustworthy face and he wears a vest over his white pirate's shirt. Although this advisor speaks to Roger, the captain does not acknowledge the man behind him, he does not even make the effort to toss an insult over his shoulder. And it would have been an insult, to be sure, because the old man was asking Count Roger to be careful in these waters. Count Roger would have insulted the man in the presence of the crew lest they would deem him a weak and ineffectual leader. An emotion that, if not destroyed at once, could seduce a crew into mutiny.

It will never be learned (because Jeremy the advisor to the Count will soon sink to the bottom of the ocean like a rock) that this was the moment when the wise old man, Jeremy of Norkington, warned Count Roger about the mythic monster that dwelt beneath the surface of the Mediterranean water. La Monstrum was an octopus of rock that rose from the depths, it was said, and crushed ships beneath its powerful granite tentacles.

The sound of shouting foreign voices does not distract Roger, but instead leads the focus away from the handsome angry count and through a large grate on the deck floor, allowing a clear view into the dimness of the holding cells below. Arab slaves look up out of the grate and the whites of their eyes appear almost comically bright in the cavern. Their mouths move and they hold up their cupped hands as if giving praise or releasing invisible butterflies into the air.

A sailor drags a wooden bucket across the deck and pours water onto the men below. Behind the blur of water cascading over their dark and unshaven faces they drink and swallow with the fury of thirsty beasts.

In a few moments, more water will rush in on the group of men. From all sides, they will feel the pressure of the ocean surrounding them, tugging them down, further away from the gray sky which they only barely glimpse now as they drink.

Their collective deaths will represent a moderate loss of revenue that King Edmond, when he finally arrives with a rescue party at the spot on the beach where his brother (the only suspected survivor) kneels in torn clothing and prays, his blond hair the image of a tempest itself, will deem a small sacrifice to pay for the life of his only brother. Instead of mounting the horse that King Edmond had brought, Count Roger will insist that they remain and send for more soldiers and slaves who will help build a cathedral to the spirit who descended from the heavens at the last moment and plucked him from certain death.

A spirit in the form of a nude woman and as Roger insisted on the nude aspect, as he described (in detail) the curve of the spirit's breast and her hips, it seemed unlikely to Edmond that they would be able to dedicate the cathedral to the Holy Virgin Mother Mary, who had, in the past, saved a royal Norman sailor here and there. No, it would not be appropriate to reveal the nudity of such a holy woman; Rome would not hear of it.

The same water-delivering sailor spends the last moments of his life, walking down a flight of wooden stairs into another part of the ship. He carries a large mug covered with a hunk of disfigured bread. He arrives in a small room, illuminated from the grate in the ceiling, and a single young Arab woman sits tied to a chair in the center of the room. She wears ornate robes made from red and gold thread and her long black hair hangs behind her, almost touching the floor. Surrounding the woman, stacked in coffin length wooden crates along the walls are Count Roger's treasures, his rewards from the most recent battle. The crates, with tufts of straw sticking out through the slats in places, are stacked along the walls. They contain statues and golden relics, seized from the barbarians.

There is a marble sarcophagus at the base of one stack; it is precisely the same length and width as the other crates, and elaborate decoration has been carved along the visible side. Strings of beads and letters the size of a fingernail cover the roman coffin from corner to corner.

As Count Roger recalled, each side of the sarcophagus had displayed the same amount of quality detailed carving. He remembered thinking that it would probably take a man at least half of his life to carve a sarcophagus as intricate and detailed as this. The dull color of the crates and carved stone make the woman, Princess Hatucha, appear beyond alive with flaming color and energetic movement even though she is as inert as the dead men inside the stone box.

Before the mass drowning and complete destruction of the ship, it was to have been a love story, a symbolic tale about the love of two people from drastically different parts of the world. Count Roger and Princess Hatucha from Arabia would have been brought together in a holy marriage ceremony at the King's Court in Palermo and in this one moment Sicily would live and breathe as the first multicultural success in all of known history. She would have come to love the brute Count Roger whose tenderness would have been brought to the surface by her touch and mythic beauty. She would have given birth to eleven children, mixed breeds, who would nonetheless occupy important posts throughout the Norman Empire signaling to the world that those people considered slaves were not so simply because of their inferior race, but only by virtue of the successful oppression of rulers. An awareness that all could be made slaves, under the right circumstances, would creep like mold through the known world. Sicily, with the Arabic Puppet shows and distinctly European Christian religion would have become the true 'island of the sun,' as Plato named it, a slave-less place of paradise and harmony.

When the sailor breaks off a piece of food and approaches the young woman's mouth with it, she spits directly into his face. The sailor angrily attempts to shove the piece of food into the woman's clenched mouth, her neck twisting and struggling from side to side.

Enough, Count Roger says. He stands in the doorway to the small room and the sailor makes one last, childish push at the young woman's closed mouth before dropping the bread onto the floor and leaving.

Count Roger enters the room, picks up the bread and places it on the woman's lap. She turns away and he studies her neck.

My own cave of wonders, Count Roger says. He
walks around the small room, surveying the crates, letting
his hand pass against the straw that sticks out in places. He
kicks one of the sarcophagi and stares down. The princess
and the stone box, he says, both sealed tight, silent, and
mysterious. Both concealing a discovery beyond
imagination.

This stone box, he continues, could be the final
resting place of a Roman mystic, a brilliant observer of the
natural world who carried into death the very meaning of
life on earth. The knowledge and power by which this man
who was said to have perished at the foot of Mount
Vesuvius, could have escaped that certain death and arrived
in your country to live another twenty years. Buried with
his secret at long last in the rarest of coffins, signifying the
influence and power he continued to wield even in a foreign
land. Count Roger crouches and runs a finger along the rim
of the lid. A secret that has fused stone to stone over the
years, turning this box into a single rock that has defied any
man's attempt to remove the lid.

Count Roger stands erect and walks to Princess
Hatucha; he places his hand on her chin and she does not
struggle. And you, are you fused closed as well, he asks.
The princess turns her eyes up and stares at Count Roger.

What do you want from me, the princess asks.

A good question. The princess does not have
information, nor does the count suspect that she does. He
wants something different from the princess; one of these
sarcophagi will reveal the power he seeks to become king.
The dead man will provide instructions, explanations, and
evidence to help the count pursue his destiny: the secret of
cheating death or else the mystical power required to return
from the dead. But what then does he wants from the
princess? Is she not part of the destiny that the count feels
throbbing in his chest?

The sarcophagus will eventually yield to the strength of men; even if the count has to smash the box and remove all the fragments one by one, the information will be obtained. The count suspects that what he wants from the princess can not be taken by force; I will break into you, he wants to say, but he does not yet speak. The question of why remains. Perhaps he is on the verge of an epiphany, a moment when he understands that anything of value contained inside the princess, inside any human being must be given willingly, must be offered in order to retain its value. As soon as it is extracted by force it turns to dust, becomes worthless and crude.

Count Roger teeters on the verge of this monumental comprehension, but his moment is cut short by the sudden jarring of their present reality and the squawking sounds of human confusion that seem for a moment to join together as the sounds of trumpets might at a Royal ceremony: an announcement or introduction of the granite that punctures through the bottom of the ship, tossing the bound princess to the floor, and seems to lift them all before gripping them (stone bursting through floors that have become ceilings, walls that have become floors) and plunging them deep into the ocean with bone-crushing force.

Unfortunately, Count Roger is never again able to approach a moment of comprehension as profound as the one that was about to occur just before his ship cracked apart and sunk.

The statue of the black Madonna with child and the unconscious body of Count Roger and are the only two remnants of the disaster that wash up on Maladu's beach. The one, carved from black cedar and sealed with African tree sap, manages to survive and intercede on behalf of the other, who will know that a miracle has taken place almost immediately upon opening his eyes.

The Path Made Ready

"Human beings can hardly move without models for their behavior, and from the beginning of time, in all probability, we have known no greater purveyor of models than story-telling." John Gardner <u>The Art of Fiction</u>

Dama walked through another rainy night. Dressed in his black slicker and black boots he splashed through the puddles without hesitation. A black bag bumped against his hip with each step.

His hair stuck to his head and rain-water streamed down his cheeks. Follow the bird; he glanced up. The enormous black form sat on top of a lamppost half a block away, as still as a gargoyle, one of its unmoving eyes shining. Warm rain pelted his face. He lowered his head; the shattered concrete passed under him.

The bird lifted off when Dama approached the lamppost, and the wings sent a burst of wind and rain against his face. A weak fog developed around his ankles and rose up around him, lifting the aroma of diesel fuel and eggs.

Dama turned a corner and saw the façade of a stone cathedral. The bird had settled on the furthest corner; the huge black eyes stared at Dama through the fog and drizzle. Warm water continued to stream down his face. Dama felt a weight in his left jacket pocket. His wet fingers touched a large smooth metal ball.

Just around the church corner, cement stairs descended to a large wooden door. Dama looked up, but the bird had not flown away. The door was a light maple color. He stared at the bright blond wood; he smelled cut tree and polyurethane. Someone tapped his shoulder. An old woman with white hair smiled at Dama. He relaxed his grip on the metal ball. She held a small purple purse clutched in her blue-veined hand, and she wore a white sweater and dress embroidered with pink and blue flowers.

"Excuse me," she said. She passed by Dama, pushed open the door and walked inside. The door closed with a loud click.

The woman, soaking wet, wearing jeans and a white tee-shirt appeared on the staircase. She smiled and lifted both of her hands to gather her wet hair into a pony tail. Rain-water moved down the inside of her arm and disappeared passed her shaved armpit. She was not wearing a bra.

"You made it," she said. She reached out and squeezed Dama's arm. "Good for you." She smiled at him. She was probably in her early forties. "Almost there now," the woman said. She brushed passed Dama. He saw water droplets on the back of her smooth white neck. He smelled fake green apple. She opened the door and paused to look over her shoulder at Dama, "Coming?"

Dama followed her through the door and into the church basement. Everything in the room, including the people sitting in folding chairs, looked used and worn out.

"I've got to change," the woman said, leaning into Dama.

Dama stood in the doorway and watched the woman greet a few people as she made her way into a bathroom along the back wall. The rows of chairs faced a single wooden podium with a black microphone and Dama scanned the people's faces.

"I see you-hoo," a woman called out. A short wide woman smiled and waved at Dama. "The Lord does not turn His back on anyone," she added in a high-pitched singsong voice.

Dama didn't move.

"Don't be shy," the woman said. "I'm Cheryl," she called out, pressing a hand to her chest. She had thin brown hair on an eggshell colored scalp.

Dama nodded and walked behind the last row of chairs toward a silver coffee urn and a plate of cookies. He filled a styrofoam cup halfway and took a few broken cookies to an empty seat near the podium.

Dama dumped the large cookie-bits into his mouth, licked his palm and then wiped it on the side of his pants.

"Thank you all for coming," Cheryl said into the microphone. "Let us greet one another, and I expect the old timers to give a warm welcome to some of the new faces."

When Dama turned, a man wearing an obviously fake black mustache and a green hat extended his hand to Dama.

"Alan," the man said and Dama lifted his moist palm and shook the man's hand.

The woman was moving toward Dama to sit in the seat next to him. Her wet tee-shirt had been replaced by a red blouse, buttoned up to her neck. She wore red boots with heels and when she moved her legs to face Dama squarely he saw that the torn crotch of her jeans was fastened with a safety pin.

She smiled at him and touched him briefly on his thigh. She leaned forward and whispered into his ear.

"Don't you worry about a thing," she said. "These people are great." She left moisture on Dama's ear lobe.

"Patrice," Alan said. The man pushed Dama aside with his elbow and affectionately grasped Patrice's shoulder.

"Alan, it's so good to see you," Patrice said with a broad smile. "How have you been, nice costume you got there." When she leaned to kiss Alan's cheek, she looked at Dama and rolled her eyes. Dama smelled strawberry shampoo and cigarette smoke from Patrice's hair, and he felt the heat return to his face.

"I find that a little pretend helps keep me off the path," Alan said.

"Have you found a job?" Patrice asked.

"Something temporary," he said. "It's still hard."

Patrice smiled sympathetically and said, "Keep of the path."

Alan nodded and responded, "Keep off the path." Alan sat back in his chair, and Dama felt the man glaring at the back of his head.

Patrice turned to Dama and asked, "How long have you been off the path?"

Dama looked straight into Patrice's green eyes.

"Three days, for me," Patrice said. Then she looked at the red watch on her wrist and said, "Well almost three days."

"Let's begin," Cheryl said into the microphone and Patrice reached out and squeezed Dama's hand. She winked and gave him a nod of support. "You'll be okay," she whispered. "You're with me."

The chatter in the room faded as Cheryl said, "For those who don't know, I am Cheryl, the coordinator, and it has been twelve hours since I last walked on the path."

"Hi Cheryl," the crowd responded.

"And I have one question for you," Cheryl paused and took a deep breath. "Who are we?!" Cheryl shouted.

"Real People!" the crowd responded.

"And what do we have?"

"Self-Respect!"

An uproar of applause and catcalls and whistles filled the basement. A few people stood and clapped with their arms raised.

Cheryl extended both hands to quiet the crowd. The noise subsided and everyone sat down.

"Let us pray," Cheryl said.

She stepped back from the podium and bowed her head. The congregation fell silent. People bowed their heads and closed their eyes. Dama mimicked their gestures.

"Dear higher power, give us the strength to resist the path that has been set before us. Praise be."

"Praise be."

"Stay off the path," someone shouted and a few people yelped in agreement.

"The floor is open," Cheryl said. "Who'll share their story?"

Patrice stood up. A few people clapped and shouted encouragement. She squeezed in front of Dama, and he felt her body heat press against his legs. She steadied herself, placing one hand on his shoulder and squeezing. She gave him a quick, shy smile before stepping into the side aisle and walking to the podium.

"My story," Patrice said leaning forward to speak into the microphone. "It's not unlike many of yours. At one time I was just a regular woman, a wife, a mother to two wonderful teenagers, a 14 year-old son and a 17 year-old daughter. I worked in the garden, read novels, nothing out of the ordinary. That all changed on the day that I began to read my trigger-book." There were a few sympathetic sounds and nods.

"There were many similarities between the book and life. For example, the narrator in the book was married and had two children and she worked in her garden. The narrator was living a normal life, but secretly, she felt alone and desperate. To find some relief, the narrator started to smoke pot during the day while her kids were at school. And, in the story, the smoking became selling and moved on to crack, and so on, until this woman basically turned into a prostitute, turning tricks for money to buy heroin. When it became clear that her children would need enormous sums of money to pay for college, the mother begins to allow her daughter to earn money, one man at a time. As I read, I was shocked and appalled by the woman's behavior. I kept thinking, how could a seemingly normal suburban wife and mother change into a drugged out sex worker who exploited her children and hid her stash inside stuffed animals?"

There was a reverent silence, a few sympathetic shakes of the head. Patrice composed herself and finished her story. "I spent a week thinking about the woman and her sense of loneliness and bit by bit her situation didn't seem so shocking at all."

"We've all been there," someone yelled.

"It felt like the story was really about my own crushing loneliness and desperate need for escape. I fell into a depression and well, the next thing I knew, I was loading groceries into the minivan and waiting for a friend of mine to show up. I bought my first plastic baggie of marijuana, but I kept it hidden in my sock drawer for a week before I tried it. My friend insisted that it was like Zoloft or Prozac, but it was more natural with no side effects. That's how I started on the path. I re-read parts of the book and then took the next step. After each step, I would shake myself out of it and promise to give up the story for good. But I couldn't stop.

"Once I found out about this group, it was easier for a while to get back to my usual, gardening, casserole-making self. But even with the meetings, I'd only last a day or two, and then BAM, I'd be back on the path. My husband took my son and moved away. By the time my trigger-book hit its sixth week on the bestseller list, I was cutting bricks of cocaine for my daughter to sell at school. You all know how easy it is, just to start right up again, like the path is just waiting there for you, calling to you." She paused and took a deep and unsteady breath.

"Last week, for the first time, I paired up my daughter, Allie, with a handsome, disease-free, and kindly businessman. Before they went at it in Allie's own bedroom; I took down posters of the shirtless male musicians and movie-star men tacked to her walls. Can you believe it? My daughter was about to sleep with a businessman in her childhood bedroom, and all I could worry about was whether he would be offended by the images of much sexier men. God, I'm a monster."

Earnest shouts of, "No Patrice," and "No, you're not," and "We're here for you Patrice," bounced around the room.

"And I know some of you are struggling with your third or fourth book, and I want to believe that it gets easier, but I don't think it ever will. I am thankful for all of the support, thankful that you all take me back no matter how many times I fall off the wagon, but down deep, I think we all know that our situation is hopeless."

The room was silent. Cheryl looked around from her seat, unsure what to do.

"By now I should probably be crying. I should be dabbing a crushed tissue to my face and struggling to compose myself. But I'm not, and I'll tell you why. Because today, my friends, is the day that we are all set free."

While looking directly at Dama, Patrice said, "I need everyone to give me their undivided attention. I know we're not supposed to mention this, but I know that each of us, deep down, is waiting for the Maker to arrive."

Cheryl stood, an expression of disapproval on her face, and said, "Okay Patrice, I don't want you starting anything. Why don't you sit down and give someone else a chance? Who'll go next?"

Patrice didn't move. "It's useless to pretend," she said. "All of us are aching for the Maker to arrive and while we'll roll our eyes and assure each other that we don't believe in such nonsense, I know that deep down, we are counting on it. We probably spend hours and hours researching the maker, learning little details, too afraid to share our information with each other. But we are all waiting for the Maker to pull us aside one day and—"

All at once, people started to talk rapidly and loudly to one another.

"That's enough, Patrice," Cheryl said sharply, and she approached the podium. Without a microphone it was almost impossible to hear Cheryl. "I'm surprised at you Patrice, you should know better."

Patrice grasped the microphone. "The Maker is real," she said. "I have brought him here tonight."

Everyone stopped talking and in the sudden silence, they stared at Dama. He looked back at them and then stood up. One hand pressed his black bag against his thigh and the other hand slipped into his pocket and tightened around the metal ball.

"He'll wear all black," someone shouted out.

"He will sit among you in an attitude of serenity," someone else said.

"He will carry with him the key to your new life," a different person said. They moved toward Dama.

"Why don't you tell us where you came from?" Patrice asked. She looked at Dama with an expression of encouragement.

"I don't know."

"Of course you don't," Patrice said. "Because you have been sent here for us, today. I promise you Dama, there is no reason to be afraid. Just take a few moments and think. Then simply tell us what we have to do."

A few people had started to cry and a few were on their knees in a posture of prayer.

Patrice still stood behind the podium. "Let me try to help you," she said. "Go ahead and tell us if anything has felt different for you since you've walked through the door. And I don't mean anything you've heard us say; I mean the way you feel, anything that you might have noticed."

"Color," Dama said. "I've never seen bright colors like this."

Patrice smiled and nodded. "What's in the bag?" Patrice asked.

Dama hesitated. Shaking his head, he slipped off the bag and held it out to Patrice.

Patrice took the bag, unfastened a strap and flipped open the top. Her slender hand pulled out a large manila envelope and then a box of ballpoint pens. She handed the empty bag back to Dama.

Patrice tore open the envelope and pulled out a large booklet. "We are saved," she shouted. Printed on the front of the booklet in large black letters were the words **Character Profile**.

The group began to push and strain toward Patrice. Dama took the packet out of Patrice's hand and put up his palm. "Quiet," he shouted, and the room fell silent. "Everyone take a seat. I will hand out the profiles. There are plenty for everyone."

Everyone returned to their seats and a few people
hugged each other before they sat down. Dama looked
around the room and then at Patrice. Slowly he walked up
to the podium and bent the microphone closer to his lips.
He pulled all of the booklets out of the envelope, held them
in the air, and spoke. "I have something to say, before I
hand these out." The excited murmurs and conversations
dies quickly.

"Right now we, you and I, exist on a boundary of
sorts; in between two possible forms of existence. This
temporary relaxation of my own confinement, give me a
chance to warn you. What I'm going to say now, is off the
record," Dama said. "I have the official instruction sheet to
read, but what I'm about to say is from me alone." Dama
cleared his throat. "I know what you want," he said. "I
know about the desire that pulls you time and time again
back onto the path. Some of you have been in jail or prison
because of what you've done. Most of you have been
married at least three times. I know all of this because I was
once just like you. And just like you, I believed that being
made into a full character was the only way to break the
cycle. You must understand that once you commit, once
you fill out one of these, your fate will be determined.

"Characters have no power to alter the path set
before them; you'll exist only as a function of something
else, some plan that you cannot know until it ends. It's
possible that you will never know what your role was in the
larger story. So I am trying to warn you; the torment you
feel each time you slip back onto the path, the pain you
endure when you step off the path and attempt to proceed
as a real person, these are nothing compared with the
despair you can feel as you slog from one episode to the
next, obeying without choice, blocked from having any
thought or any idea that does not suit your higher purpose.
If there is anyone who doubts their conviction, I am here to
tell you to leave before you decide to enter into this
slavery."

Silence. People stared up at Dama from their seats.

"Some of you want this. You want to be controlled and used and made to act in a certain way, made to think pre-designed thoughts. You imagine that by surrendering yourself, you will find relief from the agony of personal choice and failure. So this is what you must weigh before you continue; do you want to give up the last threads of your freedom in exchange for the security of your limited and pre-determined fate. Understand that once you have been Made, the chances of coming into contact with the real world, ever again, is beyond remote. The Makers are the only exception and even this, I've learned, only deepens the despair, because we are able to see all that we have lost. I assure you, if it was offered, there is not a single individual who would not immediately return to your real existence. Who now, would like to fill out the profile?"

Dama stood back from the microphone. After a few moments of quiet, someone near the back raised their hand. One by one, hands appeared in the air and Dama walked around and distributed the profiles. He paused in front of Patrice and her raised hand. He shook his head and walked passed her without giving her a profile.

Patrice leaned back in her seat and crossed her legs. She kept her hand held high.

Everyone in the room requested a profile form and Dama stood in front of Patrice, holding the last form in his hand. He looked at her and shook his head again.

Patrice nodded vigorously, lunged forward and yanked the form from Dama's hand. Dama stared at her for a long time. Then he picked up the box of pens and sent them around. Dama picked up the sheet of paper that he'd left on the podium. Printed at the top were the words, **Read Aloud Before Beginning:**

Dama read: "By filling out the information in the
character profile, you are committing yourself to the
transformation process. You certify that your answers are
true and detailed to the best of your ability. Some of the
questions are extremely personal and intimate, and these
details are essential in developing a character that will suit
everyone involved. By submitting this profile you agree to
participate in the process. Thank you for your attention to
detail, and for your cooperation."

Dama looked up. Heads were bent over their
profiles, pens moving. He sat down in the chair and stared
at Patrice, who was bent over her paper, the tip of her
tongue pressed against one corner of her mouth as she
wrote.

After slipping the forms into his black bag, people
returned to their seats. A few of them closed their eyes and
let their heads tilt back or to the side. When Patrice was
finished she walked over and knelt to slip her paper into the
bag. She leaned forward, pressed one hand on Dama's
thigh and gently kissed his lips. When she turned to walk
back to her seat, Dama picked up the bag and set it on his
lap. He put his hand inside the bag, took Patrice's form in
his hand, and folded it once and then again. While he
folded, he moved his lips as if he were counting. He folding
it over until it fit inside his clenched fist. He pulled his fist
out of the bag and pushed the folded paper into his jacket
pocket.

Once all profiles and pens had been turned in, Dama zipped up the bag and read from his instruction sheet. "Once all profiles have been completed, the Maker will deliver the profiles for authentication. This process will take no longer than thirty minutes. As we will need to match your voice and speech patterns with your record, the Maker will leave the necessary communication device in the room. When you hear your name called, please speak loudly and clearly; you may answer the questions from your seat. All others are asked to maintain complete silence. Thank you for your cooperation.

"Please move your chairs into a tight circle," Dama said. He placed an empty chair in the center of the circle, took the metal sphere from his pocket and placed it on the seat. He looked at Patrice and said, "Regulations require that someone accompany me on the delivery. Would you be so kind?"

Patrice smiled and blushed. She stood and bounced a little on her knees. "It would be my pleasure," she said.

Dama looked at Alan and then at the metal ball. "Will you take care of that?"

Alan smiled broadly and nodded. "I would be honored."

"After we leave, wait five minutes and then press the button," Dama said. "That will connect you with headquarters. After a few minutes, you should hear a voice testing the connection." Patrice was hugging some of the people in the room and laughing with others. With the bag over his shoulder Dama gripped Patrice's arm and led her out the door and up the cement stairs. The rain had stopped and he scanned the night sky until he saw, a few blocks away, the black bird perched on top of a missile-like stone monument. Dama pulled Patrice and started to jog.

"What are you doing?" she asked, still smiling, her words bouncing.

"Saving you," Dama said.

The explosion happened when they were only a few blocks away from the church. The ground vibrated.

Patrice stopped, "What happened? What's wrong?" She stared at the smoke pouring out from under the church.

"Nothing's wrong," Dama said. "We've got to keep going."

The black bag had vanished from around Dama's shoulder. He felt Patrice's folded profile safe in his jacket pocket, and he grabbed her wrist and pulled her along.

"Should we go back? Maybe they need help," Patrice said, looking over her shoulder as she ran.

Dama yanked Patrice into an alley. He stepped into one of the several doorways and pressed himself flat against the door. "Keep quiet," Dama said.

"What are you doing?" Patrice asked in a whisper.

Dama turned to look at Patrice; he smiled. He leaned forward and kissed her. After a moment, she kissed him back. "I'm escaping," Dama said. "And I'm saving you from making the biggest mistake of your life."

They waited, standing, in complete stillness, occasionally whispering to one another until the night sky began to lighten. When sunbeams shot pink across the sky, Dama reached out and took Patrice's hand in his. "We need to get as far away from here as we can," he said.

"Is it safe?" Patrice asked.

"Stay close," Dama said. He led Patrice out of the doorway. They crept, slightly hunched, down the alley toward the main street. Dama stepped onto the sidewalk and looked down one side of the street and then down the other.

A deafening animal shriek blasted through the sky. Patrice screamed.

Dama looked up and saw the bird dive toward them. The head grew larger and the beak opened. The blackness of the throat expanded as the bird approached, eclipsing the sky into night. Dama closed his eyes; Patrice pushed her head into his chest.

Dama felt a slight breeze before the darkness swallowed them whole.

Metafiction and You, Dear Reader

One of the first objectives of metafiction was to expose the expectations of the reader and the process of reading. This exposure resulted not only in a better understanding of narration, but also in the awareness of the inherent expectations we had as human beings in all situations of our experience. Our understanding of what makes up a story had become so ingrained in our way of understanding that it had become buried, fixed, and perpetually reinforced by our natural preoccupation with the past. The first and most obvious way that this 'fourth wall' (as it was often called by playwrights) was broken was when the author spoke directly to the reader from within the text. John Barth makes it quite clear to whom the narrator is speaking in this story "Life-Story":

> The reader! You, dogged, uninsultable, print-oriented bastard, it's you I'm addressing, who else, from inside this monstrous fiction. You've read me this far, then? Even this far? For what discreditable motive? How is it you don't go to a movie, watch TV, stare at a wall, play tennis with a friend, make amorous advances to the person who comes to your mind when I speak of amorous advances? Can nothing surfeit, saturate you, turn you off? Where's your shame? (Funhouse 127)

The reader has now become as much a part of this John Barth story as possible. They've called to mind the television, the idea of tennis and associated knowledge, the concept of amorous advances and associated images, reflections, desires and memories. While John Barth attempts to berate the reader into participation, Italo Calvino applies the opposite technique in *If on a winter's night a traveler.*

> "You are about to begin reading Italo Calvino's new novel, *If on a winter's night a traveler.* Relax.
> Concentrate. Dispel every other thought.
> Let the world around you fade. Best to close the door; the TV is always on in the next room. Tell the others right away, 'No, I don't want to watch TV!
> (Winter's 3)

This conversation between author and reader has several consequences. The reader can no longer act as a passive voyeur or receptor of information. They are drawn into the story and expected to, on some level, provide the missing elements in order to extract the meaning that had traditionally unfolded before their eyes. Their imaginations have been provoked and their perspectives readied to mesh with what the story has to offer. In many ways this effort reveals the Metafiction writer's ultimate desire to make their created thing into a living experience.

While the 'Dear Reader' device had been employed by many of the omniscient writers in the past, it had not demanded much from the reader, and had operated more as a narrative guide than as a provoker of thought.

This next quote from a secondary source, intended to draw on someone else's authority and use that to help prop up my own measly claims, is from Patricia Waugh. She is, among other things, a person who has read and written extensively on Metafiction and has not once ever mentioned the idea of imagination consciousness wrote:

> Calvino's novel *If on a winter's night a traveler*,
> addresses the reader in the second person and
> explicitly discusses the supremacy of his or her
> activity in realizing the text imaginatively. The 'Dear
> Reader' is no longer quite so passive and becomes in
> effect an acknowledged fully active player in a new
> conception of literature as a collaborative creation
> rather than a monologic and authoritative version of
> history. (Waugh 68)

Metafiction changed the role of the reader, and as in
John Barth's *Lost in the Funhouse*, it served to make the
reader much more aware of the process of storytelling (and
story reading) and to expose the story as a constructed
thing, an artifact.   But grabbing the reader's attention was
only the means by which he could explain in conventional
detail how fiction was supposed to be made.   He articulates
the rules.

At the very beginning of the story "Lost in the
Funhouse," John Barth simultaneously disrupts the reader's
expectations, explains a specific characteristic of writing,
and stops abruptly with a play on words that forces the
reader to focus attention on the actual meaning of an often
overused turn of phrase.

> For whom is the funhouse fun? Perhaps for lovers.
> For Ambrose it is *aplace of fear and confusion.* He has
> come to the seashore with his family for the holiday,
> *the occasion of their visit is Independence Day, the most
> important secular holiday of the United States of America.*
> A single straight underline is the manuscript mark
> for italic type, *which in turn is*   the printed
> equivalent to oral emphasis of words, phrases as
> well as the customary type for titles of complete
> works, not to mention.(Funhouse 72)

This exposure causes a certain discomfort in the mind of the reader and provides the initial, most accessible jolt to the reader's process of comprehension. Reading for comprehension begins to require more of the reader; they receive the tools of fiction creation so that, as they read, they may continue to make the story, using what hints and bits the author has dropped in their path. Learning the formula in arithmetic is the first step to identifying the parts and eventually unlocking the problems and Barth explicitly provides the literary formula. He explicitly lays bare the process of reading as the reader simultaneously learns the basic 'how-to-write' descriptions and watches as Barth distorts, disrupts and otherwise deflates their power.

His discussions of italics, for example, also bring to the surface another of metafiction's concerns: representation. By presenting and decoding what certain fonts or marks on the page mean, Barth is describing a system of signs, many of which carry a coded meaning. Italics and underlining are two of the most obvious, but Barth cannot help but emphasize the idea that fiction (and reality) is made up of many symbols, words or marks that stand for some idea or represent a concept. Quotations signal that a voice is being projected out loud, words are supposedly being carried on air from mouth to ear drum.

As is characteristic of metafiction, the overabundance of an element serves to destabilize the traditional arrangement. Over plotting occurs in an attempt to deflate the common power that used to come from the climactic moment. The movie *Forrest Gump* is one such metafiction which bounds from one climax to the next, thus defying the traditional story structure. But metafiction is also quite adept at eliminating expected elements in order to disrupt the narrative. Breaking the form of narrative is another way in which the reader is prodded out of their passive role.

Jose Saramago has developed a style which completely avoids the use of the quotation mark to signify conversation. He does not even begin a new paragraph for each new speaker. Instead he allows the language to flow across the page, separated only by commas so that the reader can ultimately match the speaker with their words.

Before I copy down the next quotation I feel obliged to tell you that it may reveal information in this particular story that a potential reader might want to find out on their own, if they were to read the book. In any case, here is the quote. Observe the effect (*quotations for the following quote are omitted in accordance with the format as detailed by the Modern Language Association for a quotation over four lines long, but in this case, it is important to note that they have been omitted for other reasons as well since it is the effect of the absence of quotes which I am attempting to highlight*):

She sat down, poured herself some more tea, then asked, Did you come here just to tell me that my goddaughter had died, Yes, That was very kind of you, I thought it was my duty really, Why, Because I felt I was in your debt, Why, Because of the nice way you received me and helped me, the way you answered my questions,... (Names 164).

While the playfulness of form has many consequences with regard to character and plot development, it jars the reader's expectations in the most physical and obvious way. What is seen on the page, forces the reader to develop a new way to understand. The signs and symbols that had been developed to indicate a writer's intent have been hollowed out or erased, leaving the reader no other choice but to try and push ahead without the familiar guideposts, collecting whatever substance there is to be had and categorizing it according to the reader's perspective or desires rather than filing it away as the author had supposedly intended.

In the quote earlier, John Barth deals with the use of *italics* and explains that it symbolizes the stress that would be put on a certain word if it was being spoken out loud. Both Saramago and Barth want the reader to be entirely aware that what they're reading are words on a piece of paper, an absolutely construction made of language. Patricia Waugh comments on this authorial technique:

But how then does this ripple in the traditional role of the reader translate into our experience beyond reading? Metafiction causes the reader to become much more aware of their role as a receptor, and forces the reader to acknowledge their participation in the interpretation of experience. This is where metafiction begins to reveal the similarities between the ways in which our narrative experience have consequences not only in the realm of reading a book, but in the much more vast sphere of 'reading' our life experience.

As the boundary between author and reader (and consequently between reality and fiction) becomes more visible, it becomes more and more possible to understand human experience as a narrative, to view reality as a series of narratives made up of history and memory, both of which are stories that require a reader's interpretation. The idea of reality as narrative, the notion that our experience is the ultimate novel from which fiction was created adds a dimension to the way we think about life. John Barth once said that while traditional fiction was said to mimic life, "metafiction is a novel that mimics a novel." How much more consequential is that statement when viewed from the perspective of life itself as a novel?

This is a quote by Carole Maso taken, as it were, out of its first context and applied here to highlight a point:

Writing, for me, is a significant human adventure; it is about exploration and investigation and meditation. It's about the search for a legitimate language. It's about the search for beauty and integrity and wholeness. For meaning, where maybe there is none. A work of fiction should be a genuine experience, I think, and not (as it most often is) a record of an experience. (Maso)

The desire to make literature that can exist as a living experience requires, above all, the active engagement of the reader. Without the animation of the reader's mind and the additions that come from their perspective, born from their personal experience, a story exists as words in a book. Only if they can be incorporated into a person can they be said to be part of a true living experience.

Just a Story

The story begins with you, in bed, relaxed and comfortable and completely unaware that you are about to ruin the rest of your life. With the same careless and subtle inattention that accompanies some of the most catastrophic errors, you are about to slip out of living and into the story of your life. Like the distracted eye that turns away from the road, or the bare foot that lowers onto the slick smear of soap, the time it takes you to make this mistake is nearly immeasurable while the consequences are eternal.

A pillow supports your back against the headboard, and you read a well-paced story. Not a thriller or a romance, not one of the 'I-stayed-up-all-night-and-couldn't-put-it down' varieties. You do not completely disappear into this story; you do not suddenly look up to see that four hours have mysteriously vanished. Instead, you pay just the right amount of attention. Your eyes glide seamlessly from one sentence to the next, and the story develops.

Eventually, you are lulled by the rhythm into a peculiar state of mind, a delicate state of dual-awareness; you are in bed and you are in the story.

To stay aware and in touch with both places at the same time, you must not stop to think, but simply continue to read. This is how you'll make the mistake that ruins the remainder of your life.

You read—

"The dying college president heard the hinges of his bedroom door groan open, and the fresh white pillow materialized like a featureless ghost, hovering in the threshold. The pillow hesitated for a moment, as if steeling itself before pushing into the bedroom air that had, at some point, begun to feel like part of the president's decaying body, as drained and dry as his deflated hairless legs. When the pillow finally crept toward President Marshall, he might have been dying in his bed for twelve days or twelve years.

"Moments of disorientation were nothing new, but the pillow's sudden appearance cut the president's last tether and set him rotating like an impotent astronaut. In a single instant, the levitating pillow had demolished the president's daily routine and in so doing, the pillow had also highlighted the intensity of his reliance on a daily routine.

"Linens were not changed in the middle of the night, but now he could no longer be sure that is was the middle of the night. It seemed like it ought to have been. Perhaps he had forgotten that he'd vomited onto his current pillow or maybe there was daylight that he could no longer see. The unsettling appearance of the pillow eased the president as close to the physical world of his bedroom as he'd been in a long while.

He felt a black and white spray of fear settle on his face like mist from a shower scene; he noticed the moist heat on his skin and knew that the sweat had, at some point, become his normal state of being. He was both intrigued and horrified by the sensation and the knowledge. President Marshall lay in bed with his right cheek pressed to his pillow; he stared in the direction of the open door and saw the ghost advance. The president could not turn away."

While you read, part of your mind notices the heat in your bedroom and it responds by imagining the cool night far above your own head. A white spark falls across the dark sky and disappears.

"But what could President Marshall do about time?
He constantly slipped in and out of his bedroom life; lately,
more out than in, and only peripherally aware of his body's
ongoing erosion. Decades ago, it seemed, he'd lost the
ability to speak in any meaningful way. President Marshall
had spent much of the time living inside memories of
himself and his life experiences; only occasionally stopping
by to visit, what felt to him like, the memory in which he lay
dying in his bed. Words no longer made much sense to the
President; he'd begun to think of them as fairies, and he
could no longer understand what they wanted from him.

"Perhaps they were simply gathering in his room,
around his bed, waiting until there were enough of them to
take him away. One afternoon he suggested this to his son
Peter.

'Urp ung aul,' the President had said.

'Save your strength,' his son had replied. "You
don't need to speak. There is nothing left to say.'" This
flurry of fairies swarmed around the President's face, so that
he'd had to close his eyes and let his head fall away."

When your own grandmother was dying, she
couldn't speak at all by the time they moved her to the
hospice. You had never been to a hospice before, and you
learned that it was a facility that provided the amenities and
atmosphere of a hotel for the family members; maybe as a
type of shield against the drooling ugliness and unnatural
muscle contraction of dying.

You remember that the foyer and hallways smelled
like bacon, and you wondered what gave these hospice
workers the right to make bacon; the smell of salted and
smoked flesh seemed beyond inappropriate, almost evil.

You did not really know the dying old woman; she
was not the type of grandmother who lived nearby, who
you saw every week for Sunday dinner, and so you didn't

really form any sort of emotional attachment to her. So it
surprises everyone, yourself included, when you find
yourself sitting in the front passenger seat of a car, sobbing
all the way to the cemetery. You cry uncontrollably, with a
fist in your mouth, trying to control the shudders. Your
silent and solemn cousins must be wondering what the hell
is wrong with you. Especially since each one of them had a
much closer connection to the dead woman. And when the
oldest cousin puts a hand on your shoulder and causes you
to cry even harder, you feel the need to explain. You
manage to say, "So sad."

But they cannot know what you mean. You are not
crying for this dead old lady, whose passing was as far from
tragic as a death can be. You are trembling and crying
because all of you are trapped inside this story. This is not
an 'everyone will die' revelation, but more an understanding
that her death is the best-case scenario, the best possible
outcome. If all goes well, perfectly and without surprise or
accident, each person standing near you, staring up at the
dead woman's particular shelf coffin, will die just like this.
This is victory, the first place finish, the death that we
should all desire.

There is no better way out.

In bed, still reading the story, the undercurrent of
your thoughts rolls on and you review the scorecard: you
and your wife each have a grandparent on deck in the dying
circle, including a ninety-seven year-old grandmother who,
when she hears that she has outlived another person,
probably leans out of her nursing home window and shakes
her blue-veined fist at death. Maybe she yells, "Bring it on,
you cowardly bully!" For her, death has occurred out of
order too many times to count.

Chronologically, you wife's parents should die
before your own parents, and by then, all of your uncles and
aunts should be dead. This is the plan if all goes well, that
is, if nothing extraordinary happens. If your wife doesn't
miscarry and your young son doesn't slip off of the diving

board and drown. If you don't start drinking again and this time, manage to swallow the entire three-month supply of sleeping pills.

If all goes well, perfectly, death will happen in natural order. The new baby shouldn't die in her crib, for example. But nothing ever goes perfectly. None of this is explicit; none of this projects onto the screen of your consciousness as you read.

"At the moment that the pillow appeared, hovering like a sentient being just out of reach, advancing slowly toward President Marshall's immediate future, he knew what was happening.

"Moments of clarity were unpredictable, and they were not much to his liking. Despite a desire to be confused, he recognized the pillow for what it was, and he also knew the identity of the blurry figure carrying the pillow toward him. He tried to scramble back onto the platform of uncertainty, but it had vanished.

"It should have been one of the home health nurses who had rotated in and out of the presidential villa. It should have been Kara or Tara or Maura or Laura, and she should have been coming to replace the soggy excuse for head and neck support that lay under his head like a deflated and smelly balloon. It should have been, yes, but it wasn't.

"President Marshall knew that the pillow carrier was his son Peter. And he knew that the pillow was not meant to rest under the back of his head, but on top of his face.

"Had the President retained the motor skills or even perhaps the desire, he might have made a noise, he might have called out no matter how garbled and unintelligible he would have sounded—no matter how unprofessional the gurgle might've sounded coming from this once distinguished leader of the community.

Embarrassment aside, it would have been enough of a noise to summon the sleeping night nurse, (surely someone was still being paid to watch over him?) but instead he made no effort at all. President Marshall lay in bed, seventy three years old and dying, while the pillow fairy eased solemnly through the air toward him, becoming brighter and whiter than anything the President had ever seen."

Part of your mind leaks out of your skull and ascends through the bedroom ceiling and into the cool night sky. The peculiar sensation has developed slowly, beneath the radar, but then all at once, the book-world has achieved equal footing with your world, but not in any hallucinatory or fantastical way.

You do not shrink and fall into the pages and find yourself sitting at a tea party or suddenly find yourself in a forest clearing astride a white horse with a sword in your hand.

Instead, the weight disappears.

Your hands dissolve and your head no longer rests on a pillow. As if you are supported by angels, you rise into the sky and look down on humanity; you observe the human race from a distance. You view both stories with this semi-detachment, yours and the old man's, as if each one belongs to the world of make-believe.

"Would this moment never end?

"The shining black smear above the floating pillow might have been the rich and luxurious center of the spirit world, casting out this pillow fairy to be his guide into the next life. But it was not. The slick blackness was the oiled hair of his only son Peter, and of that the president was unhappily certain. This was no exchange of linens, but a surrender of spirit, or even grittier than that.

"The pillow hesitated in the air, perhaps somewhat shocked at the president's quiet posture. After all, the president's eyes were open, his head resting on one cheek, and he stared directly in the pillow's general area. President Marshall had not been a quiet and complacent man by nature—he had been a fighter, and the nurses had repeated this at the beginning, a real bear of a man whose strength of will and brilliant vision for the future would see him through to recovery. He was still a young man, they'd said, still had so much to offer the community.

"But they were paid, his son had remarked more than once, to kiss his ass. At the moment of the pillow's appearance President Marshall was no longer a bear; he weighed less than ninety pounds and his outer skin shed so frequently that a special dustpan had been placed at the foot of his bed."

You empathize with the old character, the fumbling human who trips and bumbles and skids into death and you think that it is a shame that these humans are so obviously doomed. One way or another. Wouldn't it be awful to be one of them?

As a watcher, you feel weary and sad, but in the same way that a person might switch off a depressing movie, or click away the disastrous evening news, you experience a moment of opportunity, an instant of choice. Closing this book will shut out this old man and his tiny human world of mistakes and emotional harm. You can turn away from this world and get some rest, no longer burdened by the line of family members waiting to die in chronological order. No longer waiting your turn.

You're so relieved to know that you will not have to die or watch others die or hear your daughter's gargled scream coming from the river. As you walked or sprinted or slid into death, it would be awful to reflect on your failures and review your empty goals, your volumes of wasted time. You taste the old man's unrequited life like bitter almonds on your tongue. And you are overcome with relief.

You peer down, an observer—you are sad for them, the humans, in the same way you might've been sad for the red ants when their hill was doused with gasoline and set on fire with a single match. Watching them scurry and burn, you felt a little sad, but mostly you were grateful not to be one of them.

"The fabric of the clean pillowcase slowly covered President Marshall's face, falling like individual snowflakes across the bridge of his nose and then his cheeks, his chin. The cool cloth seemed to enshroud his entire head. The gentle touch would only gradually increase in pressure, eventually, and the sensation at first would not prove to be at all savagely painful or grotesque. Somewhere in the president's mind, large white swans flicked across a black pond."

It is only a story.

How had you been so foolish as to take the stories seriously? This is the thought that hangs like a banner behind everything else in your mind. At the moment, you are not consciously tricking yourself. You are not consciously doing anything. The fact of the moment is that you are free to close the book, turn off the light and disappear.

These poor humans in the story, on the other hand, are doomed to live out their destiny. They are forced to watch their mothers and fathers contract cancer and wither away; fated to stand in the cold night air, bare feet pressed to the gravel, watching their house burn to the ground.

There is only one way out of their life. And they must go through it. No matter what.

Young daughters become pregnant and uncles shoot themselves in the head, and these human people must endure or take matters into their own hands. Either way it's not a pleasant situation.

You shiver for these humans, these characters in the story. You pity them.

This book-closing decision is not imaginary; it is not make-believe. You do not think wouldn't it be nice if I could just shut this book…No, such is your state of mind that your freedom, your epiphany, is as real and as inescapable as gravity: it is only a story.

With one simple motion you'll be able to turn away from this putrid world and sink into your pillow-world of eternal safety. Once you close the book, the story is over. You are swimming in the relief, embracing the sudden knowledge that you no longer have a long way to go. You are not trapped in the story, you are not fated; you are not destined to experience any of this human misery. How had you missed this realization for so long? Why had you believed yourself to be one of them? Reality has re-arranged itself, as your eyes have been moving along the words, and it is clear to you, beyond doubt, that they are both just stories. Being human is only a story; it is only make-believe. And thank god for that.

A vaguely familiar fear quiets and you enjoy a particular sensation, an exhausted elation, as if you'd remembered your back-up parachute just in time. Pull the cord, shut the book, and you are no longer afraid. You will not have to do your time. It will be okay after all.

This all happens in a single, elongated instant—a century wrapped in a second. You hold safety in your hands. You are about to escape. And you finish reading

with a light heart, wrapped in a safety that must have
slipped your mind. It is only a story, you think, and as your
eyes move over the words, the first itch of the impending
catastrophe makes its presence known. Somewhere far
away, you sense the unpleasant tang of something not quite
right, waiting for you. Your only clue is a thought that
flashes too quickly to be understood, like the flare of red
neon just before the sign goes black. You are left only with
a single question, which is the story? The answer waits for
you to finish and you read on:

"President Marshall knew that at one time he would
have been able to explain his son's action. There was a
process by which he could surround moments with words
and assign meaning to a situation. He'd done it all the time,
but now he could not even recall the first step. It seemed
bizarre to the President now, this impulse to pad words
around a moment; had it ever really worked? Words as thin
and as transparent as fairies, zipping around an action; what
could they ever have possibly accomplished? Moments
simply happened, like this one, and no wheelbarrow full of
words could do anything about it.

"This was the idea that occurred to President
Marshall as he smelled his son's cologne—a sweet mixture
of pine and rose. And it was this truth that prompted him,
at long last, to cry out into the fabric that at first settled
gently on the tip of his nose. Not in order to save his life,
but to make an argument against words. You see, he would
say to his son, there is nothing that can be said; there is no
need for framing or posturing with babble. Already I'm
beginning to loosen inside my skin like a foot inside a snow
boot, ready to slip off.

"Just then, President Marshall felt his body, against
his wishes, begin to resist the pillow.

"It was a sad fraction of an instant and President Marshall attempted to calm his body, to send signals through his nerve endings into his skin and physically convince himself to succumb. This was the best ending he could have hoped for, and he worried that it would slip away. He moved suddenly, raising one hand to his face where he felt his son's hand gripping into the pillow. The warmth from Peter's hand felt like his own, as if he'd touched his own skin. The action must have startled Peter and for a fraction of a moment, the pillow-pressure on his face relaxed. No, the old man thought, and he might even have made a sound—but the only fear rising in his heart at that precise moment was that his son or the pillow would fail to finish the story and retreat prematurely into the blurry corners of his bedroom."

Maybe it's a fruit fly that bobs drunkenly in front of your eyes. Or the heat that comes on with the crackle of metal or the refrigerator's compressor that clunks to life in the kitchen. Perhaps your pregnant wife gets up to go to the bathroom.

Whatever the specific cause, in a single breath, you have fallen back into your head. Your hands shake as you close the book and lay it on your chest.

Fear ignites each cell of your body and your skin flushes with fever heat. You peel away the blanket and the bed sheet. You feel the sweat soaking into the pillow behind your neck. Your heartbeat pounds like a sprinter in your ears. In one instant you understand that there is no parachute, let alone a backup.

The heat inside your chest moves up, tightening the back of your throat, and burning behind the bridge of your nose; your eyes fill with tears. You open your mouth wide and struggle to catch your breath. A mantra from childhood repeats in your mind, It's not real, It's make believe, It's not real, It's make believe. Instead of cooling your fear, the words feed the furnace. Your story was not real. Your ability to escape was make-believe, just a tiny bit of impromptu fiction put together in your imagination. Terror sinks deeper into you like a black cat settling into a favorite cushion.

Even though your lamp is still on you are powerfully and uncontrollably afraid of the dark. You blink hot tears down the sides of your face and they pool in the hollow of your throat. You are so goddamn scared that your stomach churns and juices with anxiety, but you are unable to move.

"Enough of this nonsense." You say this out loud to break out of your paralysis and put this childish sensation in its place. You have to work in the morning. You turn to look at the clock on the bedside table; if you fall asleep immediately, you can get a solid five hours. You lean to place the book on the nightstand and click off the lamp. You stretch your arms and legs; you shrug your shoulders, and tilt your head from side to side.

You settle into bed, on your back, and after a few moments, you place one palm on your chest and take a deep, shaky breath, but your body won't relax. Your muscles are tensed to run and your heart gallops in your ears.

The story ends with you in the dark, on your back and sweating in bed. You stare wide-eyed at the ceiling; tears rise like a tide and overflow down your cheeks.

There is nothing you can do.

Be Good

Jenna's father drove her to the airport. She was on her way to study in Rome.

"Be good," he said.

Jenna will meet the Italian policeman at the Trevi Fountain. He'll take a picture of her throwing a coin over her shoulder.

"Be good," he said by which her father meant, *"I know those men. You better not find yourself buzzed from a few glasses of red wine, riding in the passenger seat of an Italian man's police car in the middle of the night, driving up some dark road and expect it to end well."*

Jenna will sit in the policeman's passenger seat. When the police car stops, she will not recognize where they are—somewhere outside the city.

"Be good," as if her father meant to say, *"Don't move into the backseat, even if that's where he keeps champagne, or flowers, or whatever other weapons he's brought. All I ever wanted was pussy. I'm part-Italian. I brought pills and vodka—to slip those panties to the side, just for a second."*

And he'll be on her, in the backseat: the nice Italian police officer with the stiff black hair and generous smell. Perfumed dress shirts. Smooth dimpled chin and black eyes, greedy eyes. Thin lips that'll suddenly swell when she begins feeling his tongue.

"Be good," by which her father intended to mean, *"I don't care if he hands you a copy of his AIDS' test, if he's circled the numbers and words and he's smiling at you with a fistful of rubbers like this should close the deal. There is no deal. Nothing is exchanged—there are no bargains, no gains. You can't expect to turn back now."*

And the nice Italian police officer will move his expressive hands, his artist's hands with thin fingers that wander, that grip her shoulders and set her firmly in place; hands that will soon slip and claw with sweat.

"Be good," her father said as if to warn her; *"Don't let yourself become a project that he finishes, a chore that he squares away before he begins another part of his life. I'm part Italian. I've completed my share of girls, nailed them to the wall, fixed them in place so that I could get my bearings, so that I could find my way and move on to something else. He's lost, we're all lost."*

A drop of Italian sweat will fall onto her cheek. He'll be inside of her and then, a quiet slow-motion moment. Before any emotion matures, before her brain collects the details and meaning arrives on the scene, a flicker eases gently into her mind, a thought passes. Her eyelids close—half a blink.

"Be good," her father had said and after a long silence he added, "And don't forget to write."

They'll fuck and just like the reader, who suddenly thinks, *I do not need to be reading this*, Jenna's eyelids will open and she'll think, as she swallows tongue, she'll think: *This does not need to be happening.*

But by then the story will be over.

Metacharacter: Characters or People

If you have used the break in subject to refresh your beverage or grab another cookie, it is likely that you have forgotten some of what has been stated before. Perhaps an entire day has passed, or even a week. In an attempt to keep the focus clear it seems only right that I repeat a certain quote by Patricia Waugh as these specific words seem to have a renewed relevance at this point. Waugh states, "Through continuous narrative intrusion, the reader is reminded that not only do characters verbally construct their own realities; they themselves are verbal constructions not beings" (Waugh 44).

Metafiction's investigation of fiction not only brings to the surface our expectations and assumptions, but it also attempts to explore the boundary between the character and the idea of a real person. It does this by developing what could be called the metacharacter; this being exists because of and as a function of process.

One of realism's chief goals was to develop characters to the point at which they seemed to the reader to be as living and as real as any person they actually knew. This was accomplished through the common narrative devices of description, dialogue, and action or reaction. Transparency was of major concern since what Realism intended to do was provide a world upon which we as spectators could look, and among other purposes, provide a way to observe and help us better understand humans and their behavior. This component, the suspension of disbelief, was one of the fundamental qualities that helped perpetuate the idea of the world as narrative.

One characteristic attributed to metafiction's agenda is this equalization of reality and fiction. Some have claimed that metafiction's intent was to demonstrate that since we presented the real human experience as a story, both reality and fiction occupied similar narrative spaces in our minds. Metafiction was thought to have accomplished this, at least partially, by drawing to our attention our role as a reader and our necessary participation in the completion of the fictive act. In fact, this interchangeability was only one aspect of metafiction's goals.

While there is merit in the argument that metafiction exposes the similarities between reality and fiction, it was a characteristic that had to be clearly established in order to be broken. The exposure was simply to establish that people had been viewing the world as a story for quite awhile and Realism was merely another window through which we could look. Metafiction's exposure of realism was not merely to show the implicit absurdity of looking through a pane, as if an author had the god-like capacity to so precisely re-present reality, but also to proclaim that our experience as people relied so heavily on the narrative story because fiction and reality could easily become confused, each one with the ability to impersonate the other. Metafiction sought to make a distinction between reality and fiction as well as to show the likeness.

One of the primary ways that metafiction sought to separate fiction and reality was by addressing the idea of character. As mentioned earlier, one of the proclaimed triumphs of Realism was its ability to portray characters on the page with such accuracy as to make them alive and vivid in a reader's mind. In his excellent collection of essays on writing Charles Baxter writes about what he refers to as the 'character solution':

> What does one do, do actively, with one's honest revulsion and disgustwith the cruelties, lies and deceptions of middle class life? Chekhov's response to this challenge—this is a gross simplification—is to show that, hidden under the outward mimes of character there lies the substance of real character, a kind of essence. Something genuine sooner or later will show itself; all we need to do is wait, observe, and hold onto those moments when they arrive" (Baxter 208).

But metafiction, in the person of Donald Barthelme according to Baxter, set about exploring the difference between people and the characters who represented them through the development of the metacharacter.

Barthelme developed a peculiar narrator who was neither totally immersed in the current culture nor entirely removed; the metacharacter is precisely this creature who straddles both realms, alternately dipping a foot into one and a foot into the other. Baxter continues, "Exiled from character-drawing, and in the midst of (one might almost say 'drowning in') cultural sign-systems, most of which are duplicitous, the Barthelmean narrator must struggle simply in order to find a location, a place to stand and speak that is not so far inside the culture that replicates its falseness and lies, and not so far outside that it becomes cold, snobby, or self-righteous" (Baxter 212).

Many authors attempted the deconstruction of the traditional character in order to discover what it was that made these fictive characters seem so real. It became increasingly clear that the reader did not identify or attach to the recognizable human form of a character as much as they connected with certain traits or qualities.

The introduction of a story in Calvino's *Cosmicomics* begins by introducing the reader to the narrator of the tale: "Naturally, we were all there, --old Qfwfq said,--where else could we have been? Nobody knew then that there could be space. Or time either: what use did we have for time, packed in there like sardines?" (Cosmicomics 1)

Here Calvino shows the qualities of characters even while he eliminates some of those elements previously considered to be essential. The characters have unpronounceable names which should dehumanize them and reduces the reader's identification ability, forcing the reader to recognize them as symbols on a written page. But even as he does this, and even as he tells us that these characters are molecules or bits of galactic dust, he goes on to reveal precisely what makes the reader identify with a character. Emotion—love, despair, hope—choice and point of view, to name a few. Without the comfort of being able to latch onto a human-like character, the reader is forced to recognize the fact that we are not drawn to characters because they are like people, but we are instead drawn to certain qualities that we recognize, whether they are exhibited by dust or moon rock or a single sperm.

John Barth uses setting in to mimic and mock the human being's natural quest for comprehension. This dilemma involves being in search of the meaning of our existence, the ultimate futility of living, a subject that has been treated many times and become well well-worn theme of traditional fiction. The 'What does it all mean' quandary shifts as John Barth sets his quest in the uterus of an unnamed woman and from the point of view of a single troubled sperm. His fellow comrades die off in the hundreds of thousands and he swims toward the Shore, inquiring about some of the same subjects that have always preoccupied the human being. Incidentally, it is the upcoming union that will start the life of the Ambrose character who we sometimes follow through the book. Thoughts on God are presented in this manner:

> One of my late companions—that same cynic with the curious fancy,among the first to drown— entertained us with odd conjectures while we waited to begin our journey. A favorite theory of his was that the Father does exist, and did indeed make us and the sea we swim—but not a-purpose or even consciously; He made us, as it were, despite Himself, as we make waves with every tail-thrash, and may be unaware of our existence. Another was that He knows we're here but doesn't care what happens to us, inasmuch as He creates (voluntarily or not) other seas and swimmers at more or less regular intervals. (Funhouse 7)

Both of these examples eliminate the recognizable human flesh form and substitute instead much less tangible qualities. The intent here is to begin to present, once again, the concept of process over an established thing. These metacharacters are not discernable in any physical way and yet we attach to them, follow them through their dramas. Why? Because it is not the human form of a character to which we are attracted; we seek those qualities, those malleable attributes that we recognize, much more than we look for hands or feet. The metacharacter is born from these qualities. But this is not the only way in which metafiction addresses character. Some authors have retained the human being, but have gone at exposing the true qualities of character by other means.

Jose Saramago, as well as Calvino, often explicitly presents the imagination of a character. Saramago uses this technique to reveal the process of being human even as he has eliminated some of the symbols, such as quotation marks, that once served to indicate the sound of a person's voice. A reader can identify with the idea of imagining a scenario and Saramago allows his characters to imagine thus creating the sensation of being connected to a character. In many cases the imaginings of these metacharacters reveals the most about them, whereas the traditional elements (dialogue, description and action) reveal very little. In the story the character imagines what could happen, and he imagines this in sufficient detail so that we learn something about the character's perspective on life, his expectations. The metacharacter seeks to be more real by shedding the traditional boxes of characterization and becoming what many call a flat character who is, paradoxically, more like a real person than the fully developed characters of the past.

"Now, lying on his back, with his hands interlaced
behind his head, Senhor Jose looks up at the ceiling
and asks, What am I going to do now, and the
ceiling replied, Nothing, your knowing her last
address, I mean, the last address she lived at during
her schooldays, gave you no clue as to how to
continue your search, of course, you could go to the
earlier addresses...So you think I should give up
then, You've probably got no option, unless you go
to the tax office... (Names 132)

It has always been said that good fiction, realistic
fiction, forces characters to make choices and it is these
choices that create drama and therefore, a solid story. The
metacharacter who is composed of potential or who is more
of a process than a product are not only flat and
unknowable to some degree, as real people are, but they
highlight the fact that a person is much more of a process
than a product. In metafiction there is no such thing as a
realistic character; there are metacharacters as defined by the
process through in which they are engaged.
      By having a character in the story imagine their
future and therefore explicitly mimicking the situation of a
real person Saramago's metafictive device begins to draw
attention to the fact that it is the process in which we are
involved that determines our character. A true sport's fan
is a fan because of how they act, what they do, what they go
through, just as a student is not a student because they live
on campus. The student must go to class and takes notes
and listen and write and so on. Metacharacter is the
character defined by process, whether it be the process of
imagination or investigation or obsession, and this happens
to mimic, in a way that realism never could, the real person.

But the metacharacter's alliance with a real person is necessarily incomplete; after all, the metacharacter is just words on a page. The technique that explicitly divorces the metacharacter and the real person (other than the printed word on paper) is the use of negation, and more specifically, describing that which the metacharacter does not see, hear, or otherwise experience. This revelation of what the metacharacter does not experience develops the metacharacter even more, but the correlation to a real person is impossible. By reading this, the reader is offered many details about the metacharacter's habits or expectations or situations that would be impossible for a person to experience.

Again, the metacharacter is being revealed to the reader by irregular means, by the description of what is not present, what they are not thinking, not desiring, etc. It is this intrusion, this impossible observation about what is not present that helps keep one of the metacharacter's feet in the realm of fiction. After all, you are a real person and at this very moment you are not seeing many millions of things; you are not hearing the bells of a church or starting a conversation about dinner. You are not experiencing any number of sensations, and no doubt there are some which would give us (were we to read you at this moment) an indication about your life-goals and hopes and issues. But unlike the metacharacter, you have no means by which to access these prolific absences.

:Mr. Palomar is standing on the shore, looking at a wave. Not that he is lost in contemplation of the waves. He is not lost, because he is quite aware of what he is doing: he wants to look at a wave and he is looking at it. He is not contemplating, because for contemplation you need the right temperament, the right mood, the right combination of exterior circumstances; and though Mr. Palomar has nothing against contemplation in principle, none of these three conditions applies to him. Finally, it is not "the waves" that he means to look at, but just one individual wave…" (Palomar 1)

Undeveloped or partially developed metacharacters have become one of the main symbols of metafiction. We read about the lives of the characters in the story with little attachment and even less emotional response. But what's the purpose of presenting characters who are more like real people, that is, unknowable and vague? Is it possible to change from drawing from life to create realistic fiction changes to drawing from fiction to create real life? One of the long-standing anxieties or frustrations of metafiction has been the attempt to make their story become more real by exposing itself and its mechanisms to the reader. In order for this to happen, the reader must become involved in the story and not simply engaged, but they must be relied upon to fill in that which has been left out. The reader must participate in the story in order to discover meaning on any level, but also in order to transform this fiction into reality.

Participation in this case does not simply mean reading the words, or assembling the concepts put forth by the author, but being acutely aware of this process to the point, in some instances, where the reader becomes a metacharacter themselves, an essential part of the story. It is an obvious point, that no story can exist without the reader (or listener), but metafiction isolates this quality by forcing the reader to be conscious of their participation. In Stephen Dixon's short story "Milk Is Very Good For You," he forces the acknowledgment of the reader's participation by using made up words which, because of their obvious pornographic context, force the reader to be aware of their role in the fictive experience.

The babysitter who has just participated in an orgy with the narrator and his wife is getting ready to leave when she says, "'Your wife has a nice funt too. I mean it's different than mine, bigger because she's had babies, but I luck as well, don't I?' I said I thought she was very good, very nice. 'And I know what to do with a menis when ic's in my south. I think I excel there, wouldn't you say?'" (Dixon 169)

This awareness places the discovery of meaning directly on the reader's shoulders. Whether by manipulating language, structure, or blatantly addressing the reader, the metafictive writer draws the reader into a position of crucial importance and makes them aware of the situation. The reader is equally responsible for creating the story. This awareness is precisely the same as the consciousness component of the imagination consciousness; the persistent awareness of our role in constructing and developing meaning.

After involving the reader, the metafiction writer must not allow the reader to completely attach or entirely identify with the metacharacter; like many of Barthelme's characters, just when the reader begins to connect to the metacharacter, the being constructed of words becomes less developed more vague and indiscernible. We can relate to Barth's sperm's quest for knowledge but cannot entirely identify with a microscopic creature swimming inside a woman's birth canal. This part of the metafiction experiment is to frustrate the reader's natural inclination to latch onto or root for a character.

By accomplishing this, the metafiction writer has begun to open methods of interpretation that have been long since buried or perhaps, never even developed at all. We are no longer able to seek models for behavior in fiction as John Gardner suggests that we have always done, but instead we are forced to re-think our situation and the impulses that govern our decisions. Most notably we are able to suspend the suspension of disbelief.

After all, if character is one of, if not the only, way to access a story, what happens when a reader is not allowed to identify with the character, when the reader cannot decipher the emotion being described in the text? The reader is no longer able or willing to practice that which has been termed the suspension of disbelief. After the disruption of a reader's initial expectations, the character was the main vehicle which would normally allow the suspension of disbelief; this in turn would allow the reader to sit back and receive the story.

If the suspension of disbelief is upset in the reader, how does this affect life outside of the novel? Is there a suspension of disbelief which we carry with us in everyday life much as we carry certain inherent expectations and assumptions?

"The compliment this man then paid me was to say
that my work uncovers that which we most fear or
most dislike, and turns it into a kind of beauty that
can be integrated into life as a whole. I told him
about my fear of consciousness, that I'm never
really able to accept the fact of our   existence,
that I find it not simply mysterious, but
unbelievable, unconvincing, as if life's a bad play.
(Hawkes)

We suspend our basic disbeliefs on a regular basis.
We pretend somehow that we are supposed to be alive, that
we are supposed to be dressed and walking into a classroom
to teach. If we were to stop for a moment, if we were
unable to suspend that disbelief and were instead, immersed
in disbelief, how would this affect our reading of the world?
How would we approach life if instead we could not believe
in that with which we were surrounded on a daily basis? It
seems that one common answer would be that many of us
would go completely insane within a short time.
    But again, the imagination consciousness is the
process by which we can walk around in disbelief, we can
recognize the façade within we live and work, the characters
whom we play. The imagination consciousness makes it
possible because it erodes the value that was once placed on
real versus fiction. If judgment is removed from this state
of disbelief then we are not condemned but in a state of
wonder. We do not go crazy, but become more and more
curious, eager to see and we open on an all levels:
emotionally, intellectually, and spiritually. We are burst
open and are renewed with possibility even as we are unable
to believe that we will continue to walk on the cement
sidewalk and not fall into some suddenly appearing black
hole.

The inherent value of the real over the fake makes little sense when we see that metafiction has clearly exposed that the more developed a character seems, the less real they are. In fact, the less we know about someone the more real they become. Metafiction helped us to know less about characters and made them more real in the process, more like ourselves. If it's true that we have always valued the real over the 'imaginary' then how will we make a case for valuing what we understand the least over what we understand the most? We can't, and so the bias must dissipate, thus preparing the way for the imagination to take over for logic as our primary interpretive mental device.

The Writer's Struggle

I walk down Main Street one afternoon dressed like a bum. Details like torn flannel shirt, scraggly brown beard, curly brown hair (unkempt), cigarette in my mouth. I squint into my palm and write in a small notepad.

A tuxedoed fat man with a gray goatee and a top hat strolls to a stop; a buxom young woman hangs on his arm. He grips the hook of a polished mahogany cane and looks me over. The woman (probably about my age) could be, but clearly is not, his daughter. A diamond tiara glitters on her ocean of blond hair. An emerald choker attaches her head to her body. She wears an ivory Cinderella ball gown, fringed with lace.

"I say, my word," the man says. "Look dear, what have we here? My, my, a real struggling writer—a live one indeed." He lifts his cane and prods my side with the fat rubber tip.

The woman stiffens, smiles, and pulls herself closer to her father-like date.

The man reaches into his breast pocket and withdraws a dollar bill, pinched in between his fat thumb and forefinger. "You there," he calls to me. "I say, my good boy—do me a favor and struggle a little for the lady."

"Honestly, Harold," the woman says.

He looks at her and strokes her hand. He stares at her, a little too long, and says, "Isn't she precious?" He turns and aims his shiny black stare at me. "What do you say, a little struggle on this fine day?" He waves the dollar bill. I could lunge forward and grab it with my teeth.

His date watches me intently; her eyes widen, her red lips part, her choker bobs once when she swallows. "Do you think he's drunk?" she asks in a false whisper.

"Come now my good man, that's the way," the man says and he bends a little at the knee, dangling the money off to the side, showing me, persuading me.

I collapse onto the ground. I roll on the sidewalk with my tongue out of my mouth. I groan and gag and spit onto my chin. I flail over the curb and onto the street. My shins slam against the back tires of a parked car. I growl at the air and pretend to weep. It actually feels kind of good, this writhing, this fake crying. I scrape my chin squirming back onto the cement.

I barely hear them as they walk away.

The struggle doesn't end, but after a while, I roll over and pick up the money. I sit for a long time with my back against a brick building, the dollar crushed in my hand. My body shudders while I watch the people pass by.

I see my notepad under the parked car.

The fake crying goes on and on.

Behold This Man

In a small garden villa on the coast of Italy, a young man and young woman stand naked and face each other. Her dark hair down the sides of her cheeks and over her shoulders, the curly tips like seaweed pressed against her skin. Freckled chest, nipples red and tender and stiff, a tiny egg traveling down into her uterus and pausing, perfect hips and clean shaven legs.

Always sunny on this coast of the world, always-blue skies, actual blue water layered down into the deep.

His shoulders wide, stomach bloated. They have just eaten a midday meal that lasted for five hours. He gags into his mouth, swallows, and goes to brush his teeth. His butt cheeks chill while he bends over the sink because even though it is always sunny, their villa is composed mostly of cool stone and cotton sheets and cottage style windows.

This is cinematic.

When he returns from the bathroom, she puts her arms around his neck and strokes his hair. She says, "I want you to make love to me like never before." She says it softly since neither of them can breathe too well, having just stuffed their stomachs with fish in a red sauce, bread and wine.

Her fingers, slender and strong, eventually work him into somewhat of a lather and lead him onto the bed.

"No pressure, no pressure," he whispers. He places the knuckles of one hand on his forehead and lies on his back, eyes closed. He groans.

Neither one mounts the other-- no one gets off or gets themselves off. No sweaty climax. They sleep separately on the bed and their palms touch.

Outside the villa a stone path leads down through gardens of flowers, lemon trees, and olive groves. Down to the lava rock beach that ends abruptly with cliffs and a fifty-foot drop to the ocean. A crater blanket of lava, a dead moon's surface that rolls and slopes like a petrified ocean.

The young woman walks ahead wearing her light blue bikini and a pair of brown hiking boots. The young man carries towels from the villa folded on one arm and pauses to yell after her. The wind mixes his words, steals them, but his tone is clear. He wants to marry her and he wants never to see her again.

White birds share their crusty beach. Jumpy white birds that fly and circle and land and peck over and over while the young man tries to get it off his chest, tries to lay it on the line, take a stand, get to the point-- here on the lava. He thinks, when I see her face I'll know.

She turns and squints. She shouts, "What?" Raises her hands to shield the sun.

He pauses and wonders if it's supposed to be like this. The warm wind whips her hair and a dark strand sticks to the corner of her mouth.

"What?" She shouts again.

It's a good possibility that she is *it*, that if there is an *it* she could very well be *it*. The two of them, the *it* of eternal promise-- togetherness. Why not?

And now facing each other again, holding hands, with a sore on his lip and a pimple on her forehead. Sleepy genitals. Stomachs digest the best they can under the circumstances and blood pumps although there is no visible proof of this at the moment. He asks, "Will you marry me?" He tosses his head to move hair that is not in his face, to do something.

At first her face brightens-- then dims. She says, "You're practicing, right? You look around at the blue ocean and the birds and the lava beach, here on the coast of Italy and you think why not? You picture my legs, you see me straddling you and you think this must be as good as any, as real as it gets. Here with everything besides cameras and directors and with me who loves your lips and you ask me, for practice, to marry you? Is that it?"

He nods and tries to maintain his composure. As if it weren't for his skin, he'd pour out onto the rock.

"Well then, for practice, I say yes. Yes I will marry you and now we have the moment. Now the scene is complete. The time you proposed to the pretty girl on the Italian coast, the time I got engaged standing on cold lava rock. Yes, now we have it and now we have instant visions of Christmas. Together with my family, all of us gathered by the fireplace, sipping wine and eating cheese cubes. The men dressed in sweaters and slacks, shiny black dress shoes. Darling cousins with bows in their hair. We have a mountain of well- wrapped gifts and a lush tree and a family argument about tinsel, about whose turn it is to put the angel on top."

They kiss. Eventually they guide themselves onto the lava and maneuver on their sides. They pull away dry swimsuits and scrape their skin. They bleed onto the rock, imprinting the moment beneath their flesh. They press deep, urging cells to group together and multiply inside the woman's womb.

*

In the Laundromat the slow whine of airplane take-off rises from the new washers, the more expensive ones. Our clothes occupy the older models; the ones that thump and shudder like motel room sex. All around me the sounds of water, pipes filling and draining, shooting like tiny fire hydrants, springing leaks. An orange light goes on above the words *UNBALANCED SIGNAL* and I must sit on one of my machines to close the lid enough and satisfy the washer. I feel a horse's body, the way it grooved beneath a leather saddle just moments before he tossed me into the dirt.

I remember being bucked off one December at the age of seven but my mother says I just leaned to the side and slid off like a cartoon. Either way the *UNBALANCED SIGNAL* has gone dark and I've achieved *MACHINE IN USE* satisfaction.

Santa Claus, dressed in a gray tee shirt and sweatpants, walks over to me and stands looking into a nearby dryer. He says, "Electric." He strokes his long beard and shakes his balding head, white hair carefully combed over his pink dome. "Horribly inefficient." His reading glasses have slid part way down the bridge of his nose. "Machines probably before the war," he says.

I nod like he's not joking, like he's really telling it like it is.

My clothes spin under me. Across the street there is a gym behind large glass windows. A young man with his legs outlined in black spandex climbs a simulated rock wall. The rocks come down from the ceiling and disappear beneath the climber's feet. His perfect butt muscles flex three feet above the ground.

"Going home for the holidays?" Santa asks.

"My wife's family," I say. "How about you?" I wink. I can't believe I actually wink at Santa Claus.

"Work," he says. "If I ever get out of here." He wipes his brow with a folded handkerchief. "Damned inefficient."

Now a woman takes her turn in the gym, climbing the wall. She chooses particular rocks and lets others pass by. Legs of muscle. Butt of steel.

"My wife is pregnant," I say. I guess Santa is sort of like God that way, inspiring. I mean if you had something to tell, he probably has a list or already knows or something like that.

Santa asks, "Boy or girl?"

"Doesn't matter to me," I say. "Just as long as he has 10 Caucasian heterosexual male fingers and 10 Caucasian heterosexual male toes." Again, I wink.

Santa shrugs. He says, "Could be here all day."

When I stand **MACHINE IN USE** continues and I am free to stretch my legs. It sounds as though my machine may be filling with water for the third time. I stretch my calves. It really wasn't anything like that bucking bronco I rode.

Santa pulls his clothes out of the dryer and sighs. He folds his pants and slides his collared shirts onto wooden hangers. He stuffs black socks, wide underwear and towels into a fishnet bag that expands. He hauls the bag over his shoulder and nods. He says, "Good luck."

"Good luck Santa," I say.

He turns and walks away. He limps a little and pushes through the glass door, pausing to watch the rock climber across the street. Sweat down the perfect bare back.

At midnight mass on Christmas Eve I fall in love with a young man. *I could kiss him*, I think, *without a thought*. I want to kiss him and I picture him naked without hesitation. I would have to say that as we sing Christmas carols before mass begins I am technically a homosexual. A homosexual standing next to his pregnant wife and just a few feet away from his in-laws.

The young man stands with his girlfriend or sister or whoever in the pew behind me and at one point I glance over my shoulder, catch his eye. I pour meaning into that glance because we are saying prayers that I don't particularly care to indulge in at the moment. I infuse that glance with all sorts of sexual positions and assumed secret desires while the prayers remind us of our sinfulness. The prayers call out for guidance from a God that dwells above this church steeple. I want to point out that I am God, as is my wife, and the young man in the pew behind me. The singing begins again.

I spot Mrs.Claus in the next pew over with her face made up to look more white colored than flesh and her red lipstick. Powder white hair and reading glasses. For an older lady she sings with power, and closes her eyes every so often to shake her head.

There is a part of mass that I know well, but on this night it presents itself to me in a completely different light. It appears on this night as a once in a lifetime opportunity, when usually it is only about praying for the suffering, the poor, the ill. I can't say what causes me to stand, but I believe Mrs. Claus winks at me and nods her head as if to say, yes, it's your turn. I am aware of my state of mind, but somehow that doesn't seem central. My wife grips my arm when I stand, but I free myself and move down the pew toward the center aisle. My in-laws must think that I am going downstairs to pee.

I was married in this church some months ago, but no memory surfaces to halt my steps toward the microphone. When I reach the altar I step up to the podium as the woman finishes praying for peace in the New Year. I begin.

"I am God," I say. People generally sink and squirm into tight balls with red faces that turn from person to person, looking for my leash. "You are all God," I say and this forces one of the more dignified men to stand. Then another one stands, dressed in a suit. I can tell they are not following my particular line of logic.

"Our eternal life is happening now. In here," I point to my chest, "is the kingdom of God."

The men have moved up toward the altar and look at the priest for a signal. This has become a military maneuver, an overthrow at the church podium and they almost crouch when the priest signals them to wait. This man may not be harmful, the priest's gesture seems to say, we can wait him out.

I hope he is right.

"Our paradise is sorrow," I say. "And joy, and buying groceries, and falling down, and dying, being born. It is not what we want, but it is everything that happens."

People are waiting for me to finish and return to my seat. In fact, I am waiting for the same thing as I hear my words through the speakers.

"I stand before you at this moment as a homosexual with a pregnant wife. In the next moment I may be a heterosexual carpenter, an animal, an exterminator. Eternal life flows through me because I am God as you are God."

After I said the word *homosexual* the men began to nod at me as they stepped forward, coaxing me with gestures but not with their eyes. I finished speaking and they escorted me down the center aisle. No one had come to meet me at the back of the church so I walked out the double doors and made my way to the in-law's house in the cold.

There is a photograph at my in-law's house. A family portrait taken two days after my wife's high school classmate shot his girlfriend and himself in the head on Christmas day. She says she was sick to her stomach while she stood in the simulated forest setting and posed. I guess people do thing like that, plan and pose and smile even if they don't want to. People always do things.

Something is getting into me on Christmas day. A nameless sensation, perhaps a type of seasonal disorder suffocation and I gulp three well-mixed holiday drinks with my eyes closed.

I stand alone on the front lawn of the in-law's house.
Inside the house Christmas continues in the right way. Well-dressed clean people cut pie with the sides of silver forks. Buttery crusts dissolve on tongues. Brains are touched by liquor, as are words, and fire reflects off polished dress shoes. General words are spoken and drift above the people, pressing down like a fog.

When I scream, my eyes shut tight, I hear a patch of blue sky rip open and fall to the grass, steaming before me.

When they come outside I am on my knees, eyes closed, and my hand grips the dessert fork handle. The prongs are buried halfway into my left breast. Blood seeps into the shirt cloth around the puncture and I remember a small piazza in the town on the coast of Italy.

I remember the post-engagement dawn, kneeling on cobblestones in my swimsuit. Sunlight brightens the sky to the sounds of a scraping broom. The fountain water rains behind me, tickling itself in the basin.

A beggar's feet walk in front of me, torn brown boots, callused skin streaked with grease. Everything swollen and misplaced. Then a plastic garbage bag, black, dragging over each stone. A laugh. Somewhere the sun and I hear and taste and see my breath, the air. There is nothing else.

"What has gotten into you?"

"There is nothing else," I say on the lawn. A hand on my shoulder and I'm sure it's my wife. Quiet on the lawn, a Christmas quiet. Death and birth locked in one second of stillness. "There is nothing else," I say again. My breast throbs. Only this.

Plotion and Metafict

You know of course, as does everyone in the audience at the auto show that no matter what appears after I pull away the purple cloth, it is unlikely to be a car of any sort. In fact you've probably grown a bit bored, waiting with the melting ice in your plastic cup, the sweat on the back of your neck, because no matter how magical of a convention center you are in, the heat from the mass of bodies is inescapable. The hush has died down into conversation and some people stand with their backs to the stage. I'm waiting with my hand gripped on the purple sheet. There is no drum roll and the effect of the spotlight has become virtually undetectable. I whip away the cloth to reveal a plain cardboard box sitting under the table. Hisses and ticks of irritation. People murmur about hurrying before the bar closes and I stand on stage next to a wooden table with a box underneath. Only a few people notice that the box is rocking by itself; small lumps appear on the otherwise smooth brown surface. I crouch and place my hand on top of the squirming cardboard.

If the first two spheres have been at all effective, that is, if the reader's expectations for a story have been exposed and frustrated and the requisite suspension of disbelief ruptured, the reader must arrive at the issue of purpose. What, if anything, can any of these tricks and maneuvers mean, what will they amount to? This pursuit of what a story means was the last and sturdiest pillar of Realist temple. The plot has not only been said to be the engine within the story, but even the reason for telling a story at all. This was the last area to be addressed by metafiction and while expectations and the qualities of characters can be viewed as somewhat inherently ambiguous, even before being addressed by metafiction, plot was never granted much space.

What happens in the story was always said to be one of the most important elements of a narrative. Even while the connection between character and plot was exposed as being an umbilical cord of sorts, there was little discussion as to whether something should or should not happen in a story. After all, if nothing took place, if there was no rising tension, no suspense or climax or (even if it was unsatisfying) some form of a resolution, what purpose could a story serve?

Even the earliest experiments with metafiction were not aimed at deconstructing plot as this was viewed as contrary to the storytelling impulse. Instead the frame narrative came into being rather early and the author expressed the metafictive impulse by couching one story with another. A story within a story within a story was a way in which the author could question first the reliability of a narrator or a certain version of a story. It served as a tool to expose the consequences of various perspectives, and how this could frustrate the reader's desire for an explicit and tidy ending. But even while the frames often created meaning by suggesting relationships between the different stories, they did not attack the very essence of plot which could be said to be the phenomena of cause and effect or action and consequence. Stories happened within other stories, yes, and even if one did not have a dramatic climax (think of the story of Frankenstein) the inner story usually made up for it with extraordinary vigor.

Narrative frames had been used long before the term 'metafiction' was constructed, but it was one of the tools with which metafiction sought to upset the traditional concept of plot. The primary way in which this was done with a typical metafictive process, that is, by first constructing the element to be broken. Writers would create a realistic frame which conformed to many of a reader's traditional expectations and then proceed to shatter it, sometimes repeating this process over and over. At one point Barth interjects, "To say that Ambrose's and Peter's mother was *pretty* is to accomplish nothing; the reader may acknowledge the proposition, but his imagination is not engaged" (Barth 75). His commentary on storytelling continues:

> At this rate our hero, at this rate our protagonist will
> remain in the funhouse forever. Narrative ordinarily
> consists of alternating dramatization and
> summarization. One symptom of nervous tension,
> paradoxically, is repeated and violent yawning;
> neither Peter nor Magda   nor Uncle Karl nor
> Mother reacted in this manner. (Funhouse 78)

In the pedagogy of writing over the last twenty years
the mantra of process over product has become standard.
Professors regularly instruct that the student's goal should
shift attention from presenting a well-crafted and polished
final product to the process by which a paper is created. In
many ways this impulse is similar to metafiction's
paradoxical goal of wanting to be two things at once.
William Gass articulates this paradox:

> In every art two contradictory impulses are in a state
> of Manichean war: the impulse to communicate and
> so to treat the medium of communication as a
> means and the impulse to make an artifact out of
> the materials and so to treat the medium as an end.
> (Gass 1970 qtd. Waugh 31)

Patricia Waugh points out that this is the central
concern of metafiction; "The expression of this tension is
present in much contemporary writing but it is the *dominant*
function in the texts defined here as metafictional" (Waugh
31).

Writing to create a solid artifact has given way to the process of writing and its connection to the process of discovery. Papers that set out to prove a foregone conclusion have become examples of rigid predetermination which has always been securely fastened to the process of logic. The student developed a hypothesis in any field of study and then set about to prove or disprove. While there has always been rhetoric designed to allow for the flexibility of change within a hypothesis, results have traditionally always been much more valued.

One of the most obvious values of metafiction is its preoccupation with the process of creation. The focus on linguistic structure and form has led to a questioning of the traditional cause and effect paradigm. The plotlessness of many metafictional stories serves to provide an alternate way to interpret experience. Instead of attempting to illustrate cause (subconscious in many cases) and the effects, metafiction widens the boundaries and consequently highlights the possibility for the value of associative meaning.

In Grace Paley's story, "A Conversation with my father," she illustrates a process much more than she demonstrates some type of conclusive epiphany. Instead of developing characters and moving through plot, the two characters interact through the discussion of how to tell a story. By the end, the daughter has told two versions of a story, but the discussion between them has shifted and become much more about her father's imminent death than about these metafictional characters. The illumination of process is a central concern of metafiction, which often denies the popularly touted 'sense of closure,' that we are expected to desire. As the daughter becomes more involved in telling her fictional story and the two debate the qualities of character and plot, the daughter becomes more involved in her own story, the one in which she has come to visit her father who is literally on his death bed.

'   Yes,' he said, 'what a tragedy. The end of a person.'

'No, Pa,' I begged him. 'It doesn't have to be. She's only about forty. She could be a hundred different things in this world as time goes on. A teacher or a social worker. An ex-junkie! Sometimes it's better than having a master's in education.'

'Jokes,' he said. 'As a writer that's your main trouble. You don't want to recognize it. Tragedy! Plain tragedy! Historial tragedy! No hope. The end.' (Paley 30)

The plotless conversation which centers on the right way to tell a story does not follow the traditional arc of a story. If change occurs in the main character then it does so on a subtler and paradoxically, more real level. This story highlights the many contradictions between the realist's perspective on life and fiction and metafiction's desire to break out of what the daughter sees as a trap. The father is the realist who wants to use the story as a way to understand human behavior, as a way to real truths that the father seems wedded to. The daughter does not see fiction's role as that of illuminator of pre-existing truths, but as a process through which possibility exists. Charles Baxter describes the increasing inadequacy or falsity behind the supposed truths that much of the traditional contemporary fiction presumes to present.

Insights, in art and outside of it, depend on an
assumption that the surface is false. That what one
sees—the evidence of one's eyes—is at best a partial
truth. That almost everyone has been mistaken. All
cults, and the occult arts, assume this to be a case.
The loss of innocence is partly a recognition that
there are depths to things, that what you see is not
always what you get. The pathos of this discovery is
well known, especially among Americans and
adolescents. (Baxter 61)

It is probably human nature to declare that the
recognizable is truer than the foreign, and therefore this
plays well into the realist's goals. We see ourselves in the
realist story, or so we've been led to believe, but the
familiarity, that belief is nothing more than the confusion
bred by the interchangeable nature of the realist's world and
the real world. It does not reflect that which may be true on
some level, but that we have not yet successfully named and
catalogued.

Real life is a plotless succession of one event
occurring after another and it is only by training our
narrative perspective on the events that we can assemble the
events into meaningful combinations. It was once believed,
as exhibited by Paley's father, that this assembly was a key
of sorts to understanding ourselves and our situation. And
this may well have been the case, but as change occurs, so
does the effectiveness of our perspective. The world in
which the father grew up compared to the world in which
the daughter was growing up was different in an incalculable
number of ways. The realist model of interpretation can no
longer maintain relevance as the institutions that brought
them into being have eroded and transformed.

The Fireman

1. Joe the fireman said, "I'll give you a quarter if you make
    me a promise. If you promise me one thing, I'll give
    you this quarter here." Joe sat on the morning bus
    wearing a flannel shirt and torn jeans. His retarded
    friends sat in the seats near me and my friend T.J in the
    back of the bus. In school we learned not to make fun
    of these people and I always managed to control myself
    better than T.J. "Promise you'll never become a
    fireman," he said to me, and he pinched the coin above
    my open palm. And well, I promised.

2. I promised to vacuum the living room, even though I'm
    allergic to most everything, while my angry wife drives
    herself to the grocery store. She has just threatened to
    leave me again, and we are both exhausted from trying
    to make something between us work. Trying to save
    ourselves. I vacuum on my hands and knees, pushing
    the nozzle into corners and brushing up clumps of cat
    fur. "Waiting around to save things will screw with your
    head," Joe told me once as his hand stroked his long
    gray beard. "It'll throw your imagination out of whack
    and before anything else kid, you have got to save your
    imagination. It's the only place where everything
    balances."

3. The only place where everything used to balance for me

was inside a bar named JUICE, with one dollar draft beers and chicken wings that dripped red hot sauce to the sound of snapping tendons. Life moved into perspective there mainly because it was blocked out by the silent big screen TV, endlessly showing football highlights. Then the waitress in the short black skirt stopped in front of my booth. "My feet are killing me," she said and she slid into the seat opposite mine. Her blond hair was pinned on top of her head and she smiled. Her white shirt stretched across her chest and framed her neck and face as if she were a sculpted bust of a woman. She crossed her legs and wrote down my order on a pad of paper. "I'll carry you," I said and her head fell back with a laugh. But I did not even smile and I gazed at her throat as I put a green bottle of beer to my lips.

4. My lips moved, but hers did not. I wanted to be honest with my wife and so I said that the affair was over and that in fact I was sad about that, which turned out to be the wrong honest thing to say at the time. Now I have trouble concentrating in the university library when I see couples walking outside in the snow and strolling behind a giant tree traced in white, like a pen and ink portrait. Branches sag under accumulation and I have trouble reading the book in my hand. I can't seem to focus on anything having to do with the present, with formulating a plan. Instead, I simply sit and watch frosted people make words, watch them gesture to be let into one another as their breath freezes and evaporates.

5. Breath evaporated on the bus and fogged the windows. Joe sat across the aisle and explained something to the retarded man who always wore a blue hat and sweatpants in the winter. When Joe jiggled his balls with his hand T.J. laughed and whispered in my ear,

"Did ya see that? I told you Joe was a retard." I said, "So what, George is a retard, too." T.J put me in my place by saying, "George was on TV." George sat quietly in the back of the bus holding a clay horse model on his lap. We knew from television that it was on its way to be dipped in bronze. The horse posed on its hind legs, and the body strained up with the front hooves clawing and twisting into the humid air.

6. The humid air clings to my skin like hot breath. I turn off the vacuum and stand on the front porch. It could be that my wife will not come back from the store, and even this fails to provide a spark in my mind. It's like I'm dead. A coyote trots up the driveway, smelling the dirt and when it stops, it considers me. I try not to blink. George never said a word on the bus, always offering his agreeable smile. He was an autistic man, which T.J took to mean 'good' retarded, and on 60 minutes George's mother showed his work to the camera. A pair of coyotes with straining leg muscles pulled meat from the remnants of an elk's body. A bronze horse dragged a man with a tangled rope around his neck, his hat lying on the ground. Emotional power, the interviewer said, horrifying and beautiful. But George, he marveled, such a peaceful nature, such a delicate hand.

7. With a delicate hand positioned beneath her, I carried the waitress. My body compressed, and I was sweating like an Italian cradling a five-foot tall Virgin Mary. At one point I rested beside her on one knee, the sides of my crewcut drenched, my whole body feeling like I was on fire. She took another order, and looked down at me kneeling next to her. Our eyes connected, but neither one of us smiled anymore. I rose to my feet like a knight, swept her up and walked to the kitchen window. Maybe she was as exhausted as I was because when she stabbed the order onto the metal prong, she stabbed the

palm of her hand. She shouted between clenched teeth and my arms trembled.

8. Joe's arms trembled, but the woman's did not. When I was a kid I always had trouble finishing my homework when I saw people coupling together in the library. The shelves of books rose to the ceiling with a ladder to touch the top. One day after school I saw a retarded woman wearing a straw hat, black sunglasses and a lemon colored dress standing toward the top with her back against the ladder. Her arms were secured around the neck of Joe the ex-fireman. With white knuckles and forearms quivering, he climbed the ladder and nuzzled his head into her lap. He continued his ascent and for the first time in my life I smelled people in the library.

9. People in the library used to let T.J. and I watch appropriate movies after school. But Joe the fireman helped us find certain adult books. "Nothing dirty about it," Joe said. "Making babies is about the only thing we haven't screwed up." The pages felt heavy from being turned by so many hands, and we flipped through diagrams of the internal reproductive systems. One day, T.J. told Joe and I that a man in the bathroom had shown him what semen looked like. He had barely been able to see it in the library's urinal, but he thought it looked like spit. Joe said, "It's the only thing men can do by themselves."

10. The only thing men could do by themselves was die. Joe said to think about death just like anything else. That just because we didn't know what happened afterward didn't mean we should go around being afraid of dying. He said, "It's the only story we have to look forward to. The only ending we don't already know." Joe the fireman was beaten to death and left to drown in

the creek near the library. A photograph of two jean-
covered legs, twisted onto the river bank accompanied
the article. In my room I cried for literally two hours
straight when I found out. And so I did not become a
fireman.

11. A fireman, maybe, but I was no fireman. Her bandaged
hand showed the barest amount of red soaking through,
and I carried her through the restaurant while she
balanced a pizza pan on her chest. "It's burning," she
said and she tried to keep the pizza revolving touching
the pan with her fingertips like butterflies, like gasps.
On television I saw quarterbacks pass footballs like
blessings into outstretched hands, connecting for an
invisible moment with their receivers. Players danced
through tackles making the other team bump into each
other and fall down like comedy. Highlights and replays
went on and I drank ice water, down on one knee again,
while she served pizza onto the plates. Our eyes
connected. All facial expression except determination
had drained. I stood and swallowed.

12. I swallowed, but my wife didn't. I definitely have
trouble concentrating when fighting breaks out in front
of the library. My wife had come to see me in the
library, to surprise me with some news that had instantly
evaporated when she found me. I stood with my back
to a ladder in the book stacks, and the waitress knelt
before me. By that time, her hand that rested on my
naked thigh had completely healed. My composure
during our fight in front of the library had to do with
my throat, scratching, holding, massaging, swallowing.
Hers had to do with feet position, arm crossing, and
hair tossing. She yelled, "I don't want to hear it
anymore," and the force of her anger set her back a
pace. "I don't give a fuck what you want," I said. My
throat burning. One night long ago we had painted
each other with finger-paints and made love until pools

of sweat formed on her belly and streamed purple and orange onto her sheets. Sheets that will probably never come clean, and that were at that very moment, seriously changing in value. She yelled, "Get a fucking life." I said, "I will." And then she backed away.

13. The woman backed away from the unmarked grave and I stood in the shadow of a nearby tree. Baby's breath cushioned the three carefully arranged red roses that she had brought to put on the mound. The retarded woman wore her straw hat and black sunglasses. She did not cry or seem to notice the dirt stains on her bare knees. She carried a purse over her shoulder and crushed cellophane in both hands as she walked backward, and finally turned away. On TV they rehearsed Joe the fireman's death for a few days and then dropped it. Nothing ever came of it, except I guess, that final ending which we can never know anything about.

14. We can never know anything about the miraculous. My wife returns with groceries and for the rest of the afternoon there is a strange calm in the house. A silence that is, if not comfortable, at least not as oppressive. I fold laundry in the bedroom. It's like I've always waited to step inside the only place where everything balanced and made perfect sense. And now I have stepped into my imagination and found that my balance and my perfect sense will always have very little in common with the world outside of me. Little to do with my wife's delicate hand, tucking hair behind her ear, or with the humid air around our bed. I will never finish with Joe because I feel him inside me, guiding my perspective. He swallows and touches his throat standing naked in a beautiful young woman's bedroom, and his arms tremble with lust and desire. My wife approaches me and when I sing to her, his lips move.

Joe said that to be a fireman was to put our (human) life before everything else, to kill our imagination and keep ourselves in boxes. Wife, husband, father, mother. I make love to my wife on the bed, and for the rest of the day we are repaired. Eventually I will appear unbalanced and deceitful to my wife precisely because I never became a fireman. My imagination has taken over and I dwell in a balance of my own design.

15.

Crushed Blue Corn

"Julio appeared one morning at the back door of the restaurant, dressed in white jeans and a white shirt studded with purple gems. As if he had descended in the palm of God. He carried a forged social security card and slipped an apron over his beautiful clothes. Before he began on the pile of dishes, he handed me a picture of his sister that he'd torn out of a magazine. She is lovely beyond description, a haunting beauty."

"Undoubtedly. Let me guess; she has long brown legs, black hair to the middle of her perfect back and dark eyebrows. Curled eyelashes frame her eyes, two pools of oil. A professional model, what luck. Are you officially engaged?"

"She wears blue and yellow flowers woven in a band across her head and tucked behind her ears. Her beautiful voice rises in the Mexican air with the evaporation of the morning dew and her song joins hundreds of others. All of the girls throughout the land sing while they milk the cows or throws seed to the chickens. The whole region wakes to this beautifully woven chorus of voices. Like maidens from the gods, their sweet song rouses the brothers and uncles and fathers. The sound renews the men's faith in life, weaves a cloth of harmony to wrap around them as they head into the fields, kneel down, and thrust their confident hands into the soil."

"His ranch is probably little more than several consecutive plots of dry dirt. Cows sunken into walking ribcages, malnourished pigs that squeal from the pieces of black rubber they cannot digest, and mangy chickens that cannot lay eggs. Probably some other starving animals that he can't name in English."

"Llamas and buffalo and peacocks that brighten the ranch with their glorious colors. The white-haired grandmother weaves traditional clothing from the feathers, and from the animal's skins. The white and brown coats shine like expensive pelts, soft and plush from the nurturing Mexican sun, the secret family mixture of grain. The white-haired grandmother is a witch, the town sorceress, and the keeper of the family secrets, the ancient potions. Pure cold water shoots up from a spring near her cave and douses the naked and squealing children in the summertime, cools the men's sweaty heads at the end of the day."

"And your poor homesick dishwasher, dying to get back to the fruitful bounty of his imagined homeland. He thinks you should go with him and marry his sister. Then you'll be like a brother to him, part of the enormous loving family. The real world will fade like an ancient map, become a theory, an illusion. A bad dream. You think you will finally be finished with your missing child James, and that the story will finally end, the way it has almost ended many times before. With a crack of your knuckles you'll be back in action, Mexican-style, a brand new man. Your final escape into fantasy with your homesick dishwasher."

"Crazy homesick. Julio's eyes fill with tears the moment he mentions his grandmother. He can taste the homemade tortillas, smell the roasted chilies. When the sun sets on the ranch it casts the world in rich orange light. The children's faces beam, as glossy as oil paint, and they play soccer, shine with sweat."

"What specifically, may I ask, did he promise you?"

"A festive celebration for our arrival. Mexican wine from wooden barrels, traditional dancing in the main square. The girls will arrive in embroidered dresses, black and red lace, the boys in black cowboy boots and black leather pants, vests. They form a circle around me, and then Julio's sister arrives, twirling her way into the circle, her leg muscles tight, her toes pointed. She leaps around me as if she were a nymph, trailing her red silk scarf behind, letting it caress along my shoulders, hide my face. She smells like roses, and her body moves around mine like a serpent. She whispers Spanish in my ear."

"Brothers?"

"Seven older brothers. The three oldest live in the States, the younger three remain in the bosom of Mexico, building their back muscles as they work the land with their young hands. Their biceps and forearms already of men. They protect the ranch, keep the mother and the grandmother healthy, and surround the land with love, comfort, security. These brothers prepare the land and the house for the eventual reunion, when all members of the family will return and live together again."

"How rich. Your dishwasher is the baby, the last one to make up his mind. The oldest brothers live in big American cities, carry wads of cash, drive sports cars, and get laid every night. Your dishwasher thinks that they might visit Mexico more often, but they can't return to America so easily anymore. An army of border guards shoot bullets into the night backed by good American citizens who shine headlights into the dark. The dishwasher has not yet experienced American life, so he still misses the desolate ranch with decaying cows and horses that bleed from the eyes."

"Buffalo and llamas and goats. The Garden of Eden, with all of the beasts roaming around under the hot Mexican sun. The oxen meander through the orchards, nuzzle the ripe fruit that bends the branches with sweet promise. Black mustangs stand next to one another, their cropped hair falling across their eyes as they bend down and drink from the clear ponds crowded with fish. Harmony. A life of balance, of proportion, of sense."

"And you're serious. You actually believe that if you take the bus, marry his sister, and work side by side with the brothers on the ranch, you'll be able to enjoy life once again. You'll start a new life with the long legged sister. A life that won't shatter like the one you're running away from."

"Long smooth legs and dark brown, appetizing in every way. She poses for underwear ads in Mexico. Real breasts and dark nipples. As gorgeous as Eve herself, with straight black hair to the middle of her shapely back, pure eyes, dark eyes that mean seduction, as deep as forever."

"Eyes like escape hatches. Eyes that you can fall into, sink away from yourself, from your memory. You think this is possible. You believe that you will slip away from yourself by leaping blindly into Mexico. Your chance to finally quit hating yourself, blaming yourself. This plan, you believe, will drown your hope once and for all."

"Fresh corn tamales, fish tacos with spiced onion and jalapeno."

"I've got about a quarter tank of oxygen left James, and I want you to stop and think for a moment, I want you to remember. When I first became your sponsor, after we'd met at the national convention, after we'd eaten roast beef and lobster tails and lost thirty dollars at blackjack, what did I tell you James? When I turned to face you and I put my hands over yours, what did I say? Do you remember?"

"You said you will always be there for me. And I
want you to come with me Maria. His brothers would
adore you; they would treat you like a queen, and serve you
beer with pieces of lime, grilled trout with lemon and fresh
tomato salsa. We could dance together and laugh and talk
long after the sun has gone down, when the cool wind
blows off the desert and the sounds of Mexican crickets fill
the air with a version of quiet."

"............"

"Come Maria, where peace reigns and your mind
can empty into the night sky."

"On the day you've replayed in your head James,
that day you walked out of the liquor store and looked into
the backseat of your car, dropped the glass bottle from
under your arm, lost your breath—you saw a car pulling
away and your heart began to race. You instinctively ran
after the car, waving your hands, but it did not stop. In
shock, you watched it recede in the distance, remembering
only the Nevada license plates. A vague and useless detail
as far as the police were concerned. Maybe six months
after the conference, you called me and told me about your
revelation. You had accepted the fact that your boy must
have been killed, and now you only sought to lay him to
rest, to give him over to heaven so that you might continue
trudging through the world. So that you could stop
wondering and looking and believing in miracles. You were
exhausted and you had planned a trip to Nevada. You
believed in the trip because the signs pointed to it, your
intuition, the license plate. Even the fact that the
conference had been in Las Vegas added to your evidence.
All arrows pointed to the same place and the pieces fit
together in your mind, as if fate had whispered in your ear.
I drove for 12 hours to meet you in Las Vegas and we set
out. Do you remember that James? How was Nevada?"

"So very hot. Unbearable. We drive into the desert and I know where to go. I've made calculations and now I follow my instinct. We pull off to the side of the empty highway and park. We walk across the burning sand. The heat burns through the bottom of my shoes. I carry the shovels and my shirt soaks with sweat before we arrive at the proper spot. Nothing grows around us and this convinces me, proves my hypothesis. We stand on the surface of death. You set up the umbrella and we dig in the sand. We talk at first and then become silent. Sand continually slides down into our hole, making it twice as much work."

"That's exactly right James. For two days we dug, moving locations every few hours. Before we left for good, before I let you lean on me as we walked back to the car what did we find?"

"Bones. Like ivory splinters from a prehistoric time. I sink to my knees and the setting sun casts my long shadow out over the spot. I pull out the bones and dust them off with my handkerchief. I stack them next to me like firewood."

"You stopped and looked at me, James. You looked crestfallen, destroyed. What was the problem then? Why did you stop?"

"They are adult bones, not dinosaur bones. Not a child's bones. A rupture happens inside my chest; I feel my heart collapse and shrivel even as the cool desert winds begin, drying the tears on my face."

"You fell to your knees and screamed, James. You looked up at the first star of the night and you screamed. Then you punched at the sand until your knuckles bled, racked by sobbing you threw down your fists, and I let you. I stood back and watched you, until you slowed, until you pawed at the ground like a doe, rocked back and forth. I thought it was part of the process, the healing. I still believed in the process back then. I believed in recovery."

"The signs vanish, my instinct becomes as quiet and stoic as the pile of bones. The puzzle I had pieced together, the theory I had derived, the maps I had analyzed, the calculations I had made—all of it, disappears like dust from the desert. Twirling away like a tornado and dissolving into air, into nothing."

"Mexico is that very same desert, James. It's hot as hell for one thing. And it will suck you in with a promise, until you're too deep to crawl out. Until you're buried alive, and I won't be the one to come down and dig up your bones. I won't even know what has happened to you. You will have disappeared from here, yes, from this country, but not everyone who vanishes from here arrives at the same place, James. There is no secret waiting room, no cabin in the woods with tables of refreshments and magazines for those who have disappeared to gather together."

"The family has a cabin in the mountains, where orange and lemon trees grow and it's so cool that you need a sweater or a sweatshirt in the evenings. They gather to celebrate the children's birthdays, their first communions. Everyone meets on the concrete patio outside the house, and steaming food is brought from the kitchen in red and blue and yellow ceramic bowls and placed on a table draped with a festive red tablecloth. Marinated venison speared with zucchini and squash and tomatoes. Bowls of rice and red beans spiced with cumin and cinnamon. People hold beers and the children run back and forth and ride bicycles around the house. They are dressed in miniature suits with blue clip-on ties, or expensive party dresses, fringed with white lace, embroidered with gold. The music comes from the house, vibrates through the walls and uncles dance arm in arm as the sun sets on the cabin. The women stand in circles and talk. They hug one another and laugh, they pet one another, groom each other's hair. And everywhere you go, you smell the citrus from the groves and the smoke from the small fire that keeps away the mosquitoes."

"Everyone carries guns in Mexico, James, but maybe you would like that. You could turn the corner and gun someone down, anyone, anywhere you want. Or you could shoot animals and kill them if you feel like it, and nobody will try to stop you. The three brothers on the ranch always carry guns, even when they go to the cabin. They carry them because they have looked down into the valley from that very same cabin and seen men shot like animals, one after the other, in the back of the head."

"We honeymoon at the cabin, lie out on the roof, peer into the night sky. Billions of stars reveal themselves to Mexico, more than anywhere else in the world. The saints and the gods regard the Mexicans as their own people, their children, and they favor them with plenty of moisture, the fragrance of fresh flowers. My wife and I sweat together on the roof, our bodies exchanging, adapting to one another, mapping the geography of each other's skin. Her flesh moves like silk against my chest, her hands delicate and strong, determined."

"Let me guess; she's unlike a normal woman. She craves constant sex and she wants it more than you, but you manage to keep up. She's only content when you're inside of her, rocking her world. Am I close?"

"The women love men, the feel of the man's rough warm skin, the smell of his sweat. To be enveloped by a man's body is like being in a cocoon. The women bloom inside and the heat draws forth their startling beauty. They unfold their wings. His virgin sister blossoms within herself like a hundred roses, containing all of the energy and fragrance of a woman. Swollen with desire, the need to connect, to grow into another human being. The union of souls, like butterflies attached to one another behind the red fall leaves. An explosion of spirits, a watershed of emotion. Love that you can taste and hold in your arms.

"I'm scraping the bottom of my oxygen tank, James; don't make me laugh with your exotic nymphet. I'm sure she revs with sexual energy beyond the capacity of the universe, James, drips with it. A gift from the gods, an insatiable beauty. Your dream woman. A woman in your dreams."

"For three days after the wedding, the new couple remains in the cabin, to merge into one being. They explore one another, touch the emotions, and meld together like a sculpture. Physical paths lead to spiritual glory. Relatives stop by to say a prayer outside; they leave food in baskets, wrapped in cloths of cornhusks. Jugs of wine sit next to buckets of cool spring water. Each mother in the family leaves a lock of hair which will be woven into the first baby blanket. The grandmother arrives from her cave and she carries with her an ear of dried blue corn. She peels away the brittle husk and the kernels shine like rows of purple gems, each one symbolizing the soul of a child. The stiff ear a symbol of fertility, the union of the male and the female, the infinite potential of procreation. The grandmother may hear us behind the cabin door, perhaps we argue or else we scream out in the process of draining into one another, immersing and submerging, but she will not interrupt."

". . . . ."

"Glass breaks, ecstasy rattles the windows and the grandmother genuflects, hangs the blue corn on the door, and walks away. She knows all we do and it is beautiful to her, sacred, and holy."

"You're ignoring the whole picture, James. The brothers in Mexico are in serious trouble with the law. One of them dies in the field, crumpled under the green plants. A soccer ball kisses against his forehead and he does not move. He feels smoke and heat rising from his wounds. He feels his soul struggling to be free."

"When the white-haired grandmother communicates with spirits, she wears a white robe and a necklace made with locks of hair around her neck. Hair from her children and grandchildren who have passed away. Green trees hide the entrance to a cave at the base of a red sandstone mesa. Collections of animal bones, poisonous red leaves, and ancient herbs are stored in hand-carved wooden boxes. She draws the future with her finger in the dirt, and paints the past on the cave wall with ox blood and blueberry juice. The dead visit the grandmother when she summons them. She delivers messages. The grandmother is the family's translator for the spirit world."

"You've heard whispers from the spirit world and the gods yourself, haven't you James? They've tipped you off, told you secrets. After the car with the Nevada license plate disappeared you ran back to your own car, scouring the parking lot pavement for clues, for something to spark your mind, tell you what to do. You tried to tell yourself a story about what had just happened. This was the moment that would be resurrected many times inside your mind and you absorbed each detail. The back door of your car was slightly ajar and the seatbelt dangled above the pavement, the silver buckle twisting and reflecting the glare of the sunlight. You did not touch anything because at that moment you believed in a full scale investigation, armies of police and citizens combing the country, leaving no stone unturned. Truth and justice and the inherent good in every human being. You believed in this so you tried to preserve the scene. A green beer bottle lay against the curb, and you saw the word "Boulder" on the label. The blue Rocky Mountains briefly accompanied the word, the vague sense of a rich town in a shadowed valley. A detail that remained asleep until you saw the news story, two years later, after you began to seriously drink again. After the official search that never materialized, officially fizzled out."

"The grandmother absorbs clues about the past from the natural world. She has learned ancient Indian ceremonies and made potions from poison, purple berries, and petrified bark. She cures the ill, calms the disturbed. She has cast out demons and brought peace to the tormented. Julio has seen her float in the air and wrestle with evil."

"After Catherine finalized the divorce she refused your phone calls. She was the only other person who could help prop you up and she turned away to grieve with her family. Vodka diluted your blood and you watched a news report about the black market baby industry. Well-to-do communities with older couples wanted babies and they were buying them on the black market. The reporter stood on the campus of the University of Colorado, Boulder. The evidence suddenly fell into place again, as if the gods had whispered in your ear, and you rose from the couch infused with hope, radiating the very joy you sought to capture. You called me on the telephone. You now knew that your boy was alive, and you knew where he was. You'd developed a different ending to the story, but an ending nonetheless. A finality. Single father launches into the world to save his child, warm his bone-chilling sorrow."

"Parents do not separate in Julio's village because everyone raises the child. Uncles, aunts, and cousins give the child a sense of belonging, a feeling of security. Everyone takes responsibility because there is a sense of pride. Support exists like two giant arms around the family, so the parents do not buckle under the stress of tragedy, they do not experience the alienation, the sensation of being lost. Even when the parents fight, the burden remains shared and light, and the couple does not dissolve. They do not shatter like a leg bone and drift in space like dead stars, space junk."

"You began with the calculations again, James, scouring maps and reviewing your profiles of the phantom kidnappers. I flew into Denver at night and took a bus to Boulder, where you sat on a wooden bench in the station with an old leather briefcase in your lap. You held a bottle in your hand. You looked at me with the saddest eyes and said 'They shouldn't have done it. He was my baby.'"

"Babies are not taken for granted in a traditional society, one that is not medically advanced, because babies are delivered at home and sometimes they can't fit through the mother's hips, or else they become tangled in the umbilical cord, blocked from the exit by the placenta. Babies die and it is not unheard of, it is not beyond the scope of imagination. Even after a few months, babies can develop a flesh eating virus and expire in their sleep. Grief is allowed, expected, and a ceremonial dance is performed. The grandmother moves inside the circle of family members, bowing and turning away from the pile of burning corn husks. She holds the mother's ear of dried blue corn and raises it over her head. Then she plucks a single blue kernel of corn from the ear. With a mortar and pestle, the sorceress grinds the kernel into a fine blue dust and makes the sign of the cross on the mother's head. The ritual purifies the mother. The mother does not despair, does not give up, because she sees infinity on the blue ear of corn she holds in her hand. The rows and rows of purple gems signify her endless potential and she moves forward, gives birth many more times. Only one small kernel has been taken from the mother."

"By the time we found the warehouse at the north
end of the city it was nearly midnight. We stood in front of
a green metal door with rusted hinges; the silver garage
shutters along the side of the building had been pulled
down and locked. Your calculations had led us into the
pot-holed parking lot, onto the oil stained driveway. The
headquarters. You looked up at that door and I held your
hand. As your sponsor, I was supposed to help you
through the process. I had already begun to question the
process, the possibility of recovery, but being there in the
cool night air, smelling the faint odor of diesel, I watched
you stare at that door. Recovery or not, I knew that I
served some purpose. We walked hand in hand, like
husband and wife, straight up to the unmarked door. Your
body shook and your breath vibrated. You thought you'd
find him on the other side of the door. Like a movie
miracle, there he'd be, sitting in his car seat and kicking his
legs, looking at you like nothing had happened. Tilting his
small blond head in question, wondering at your distress, at
the lines of panic carved into your forehead, the sadness
under your eyes. The door opened and we stood in an
empty warehouse, abandoned, barely lit by starlight and
without even a trace of what it had once housed. You did
not scream or strike out. Instead, you fell to your knees
with your face in your hands, and I knelt behind you and
held you together with my arms. I squeezed tight so that
you might not rattle into pieces and roll along the concrete
floor, into the darkest shadows. You vibrated through my
chest and into my heart. It was the last time I would even
think about the process. Recovery would never happen for
you, or me, or any of the people we met at that conference.
It was not possible."

"The Mexican brother's look out for one another. They protect each other. If a bandit injures one in the group, the rest grab their guns and baseball bats and set things right. If something so dear and so precious is stolen from one member, the reaction is quick and severe. The bandit's head is bashed into rotten peach pulp. The brother's dance in ceremony on his twitching torso."

"You want to be part of that group, a member of their gang. Don't you see that they want you to run special errands to the United States? They expect you to dodge bullets and deliver packages to the oldest brother

"Once in a while I would be sent to America to deliver presents from Mexico to Julio's brothers in the cities. They cannot find fresh tortillas or exotic hot peppers and so I'll have to keep these hidden from the guards. Food is not allowed across the border, but I'll smuggle in pints of rich venison chili as well, maybe some fried cinnamon dough, still warm. It's a way to keep the family unit together, maintain the intimate relationship. The brothers would kiss me on the cheek and embrace me after my journey. They would give me cold beer as they opened their packages, and pat me on the back, impressed by my accomplishment. Small wooden Mexican dolls and brightly colored slippers. Bits of their homeland to keep them connected, keep them alive. I would do it as a favor for my new family, for my wife, my children. My honor. Just to prove that I was in solidarity with them, that I wasn't some wishy washy gringo."

"You still don't see it. Before they shoot the one brother, all three brothers are kicking a soccer ball back and forth in a giant field of marijuana. Their faces are partially covered by the field of tall pot plants and they duck and hide and tackle one another. Their rifles sit on the ground at the edge of the field. They roll around and laugh so loud that they do not hear the garbled announcement over the bullhorn. The message that informs them that the U.S. drug agents are raiding their field. They wrestle and laugh until they hear the first gunshot, like a rocket into the sky. They roll to the side of the field and pick up their guns. They crouch low and hold their breath. One brother puts his knee on the soccer ball and waits."

"It's a passion, soccer. The endurance that it requires, the sculpted muscle tone it develops. The development of the foot skills is tantamount to practicing magic, and so their soccer heroes are not merely men, but wizards. The people worship the supernatural physical skill and they understand the high degree of intelligence and physical fitness involved in a team's success. They live for this game."

"Since the brothers miss the announcement in Spanish that tells them to put down their weapons and raise their hands high above their head, the brothers think they are under attack by bandits looking to loot their crop. They hear voices approach and another gun shot into the clouds. Without looking at one another, the three brothers aim their guns and fire into the field."

"It's true that fights break out all the time in Mexico, but they are not filled with homicidal rage. They understand the ebb and flow of emotion. At one moment, two brothers scream at each other as if the world has come to an end. They threaten to tear the other's head off, beat him to death with his own arm. And then slowly, the anger subsides, and the two brothers toast one another with a fresh beer. They put their arms around each other and laugh. All is forgotten, understood, forgiven. They know what it means to be human, to struggle with the complexity of our emotions."

"It's as if the marijuana plants fire back. Bullets fly through the air and one brother takes three bullets in the chest. The soccer ball slips out from under his knee and he falls to the side, crumples onto the ground. The ball rests against his forehead and air makes no inroads into his lungs. Gunshots explode like strings of firecrackers and another brother is hit in the shoulder. Then abrupt silence, smoke rises, and the U.S. agents emerge from the green plants with guns drawn. Two agents have been killed and the surviving brothers are kicked repeatedly in the stomach and in the face. Blood pours from their mouths and the agents kneel on their backs, tighten handcuffs that feel like razor wire. They are punched in the stomach when they stand and the brother that vomits is slapped across the face. One agent says the boys shouldn't have been kicking a soccer ball in a field of pot. The brothers are dragged into a van and taken to a Mexican jail."

"They can kick the ball wherever they like because there are no ridiculous rules. On the road, in the fields, wherever. No regulations, no forms to fill out. There aren't even any stoplights in the small town, Maria, or painted lines on the roads. These people live in freedom. They are not bound by imaginary rules like we are. They make common sense decisions, based on what's best for them. No adherence to arbitrary laws set down by some rich politician. Real freedom to live as they see fit."

"And you're not feeling very free right now, is that it? You're feeling more trapped than ever? I'm basically out of oxygen, James, so I'm going to talk softly. The other day when you got that piece of junk mail, the one with the photograph of your boy on it, the one put out by the foundation asking if you've seen these children, you didn't sink to your knees. What did you do?"

"I stared at the picture and my heart stopped. The one second I hadn't been thinking about him and there he suddenly was, staring me in the face, reminding me that there was no escape. Rage soared inside my chest. I smashed the mailbox off of its post with my fist. I walked into my house and climbed the walls, tearing at everything like an animal. I unloaded the dishwasher by pitching glasses through the kitchen window. Plates flew like discs into the opposite wall. I went crazy, I let myself go. I fell down at one point and lay on the ceramic dust, the glittering pieces of glass. I rolled from side to side with my baby's picture in my hand and I groaned."

".............."

"After a couple of days, the restaurant manager sent Julio to check on me and I was still on the floor, weeping without tears."

"And Julio couldn't get you to move, he couldn't get you to respond to him, so he sat down on the floor next to you and told you stories. After a while you began to hear the stories and then you eventually sat up, accepted a glass of water. Then it came to you, another way to finally end this goddamn story, to put your baby to rest."

"I want to have children, babies I can hold on my lap, lift up to my nose. They love big families, so maybe I'll have ten or twelve kids, all running around, patting me with their tiny hands, kissing me on the cheek. Like swimming in a pond of young bodies, my children's limbs caressing my soul, running their small hands through my hair. They will grow and marry and return to kneel around my bedside as I die, praying for my eternal rest."

"The family makes their money from the weed, James, can't you see that? Not by selling dying pigs or starving cows or molting chickens. Now you see why they are wealthy. They send Julio to work on their next American outlet, a drug port that his family can service."

"Sometimes they sell livestock at the market on Saturday. Wicker baskets full of the least bruised tomatoes, ears of pale blue corn, and stunted and deformed chili peppers. Americans smoke tons of pot, Maria, the country is like vacuum. Maybe the brothers just grow a little on the side, throw it up in the air, and watch it disappear. They sew the wads of cash into their mattresses to pay for weddings and first communions. The Mexicans are intelligent because they never touch the stuff. Julio says it makes a person crazy."

"The U.S. gets into the act and demands that the brothers be sent to Texas where they will pay for killing those two agents. Right now they sit in some dingy Mexican jail cell eating sticky rice and cold chicken. They have only one chance. The brothers might accidentally escape, if you reach deep into you pockets James, and pays the police well."

"The brothers have had fistfights before. Boxing matches that took place while they screamed at one another, threw curses and punches. I watch two of them dance like prizefighters in the dust, and I wait for the moment when their energy dissolves and they finally smile at one another with blood on their teeth. Maybe I'm standing too close to the fight."

"Listen to me James, you have to believe it. They take your money and then load you up like a donkey with saddlebags of pot and whip your ass until you scamper across the border. You die alone James, no children at your side, no adults saying prayers by your bed."

"Without warning the brothers swallow me in their flurry of fists and shouts, and I try to duck, but knuckles connect into my stomach. My chin bounces off a knee as I fall and a forearm delivers a chop to the back of my neck. I land in the dust and turn on my side, spitting dirt and blood from my mouth. How can this be? When I look up, they are not fighting one another and suddenly they never were. They fall on me with open, salivating mouths. Sharp teeth. I close my eyes and do not wake up. I cross the final border, alone."

"The guards shoot you as you run across the border with your backpack full of weed. This is only a couple hours after you've paid the cops and freed the brothers. They shoot you before you ever get to see the sexy sister."

"It's simply life, Maria. The women's chapped hands make tortillas, mixing drops of blood and tears and sweat into the dough. They try to sing traditional songs, but lose the words among the cackle of vultures that descend on a cow. The women wear wilted yellow and blue flowers in their hair, and they smell like acrid sweat, like discarded lilacs in a sweet moldy heap. They must create a sense of pride."

"You could be stabbed as you walk on the streets of Chicago to make a delivery to one of Julio's brothers. A knife in and out of your gut and you sink to your knees. Your backpack is stripped from your body. A foot kicks you in the head, knocks you over, and your blood forms a puddle, but you don't die. You lose the package, but escape with your life. Do you think your new family rejoices and embraces you because you have cheated death? They condemn you as a fool and a traitor because you have brought a fate onto them that cannot compare to the U.S. agent invasion. They blame you for destroying their lives; they curse you as they die."

"The red bell peppers burn black Maria, in an old stone fireplace. Drunken men stumble and cannot link arms to dance during the hazy dry sunset. They drink beer and vomit in the bushes, wipe their mouths and pretend to kiss the young girls. Women gather in separate circles and spread gossip about the others, raise questions about which boy is gay, which girl is a whore. A little girl with black hair wears a lace white dress and sneers at the drunk who lunges for her bare legs. She twirls away, a frayed pink ribbon in her hair."

"My oxygen tank is empty James and I'm having a little trouble, but now you're beginning to see, aren't you? Now it's coming clear. A drug lord owns your family's operation as well as a hundred others around the region. The drug lord comes down hard on drug runners who lose packages and live. He thinks you've betrayed him, sold the goods out from under him. Lessons must be learned, examples set. He and his men visit your beloved ranch on horseback. He lines up the fathers and brothers and uncles behind the main house and shoots them like animals, one by one, in the back of the head. He laughs and orders his men to drag away the sisters, the aunts, the mothers. Other ranchers eventually find the women's' naked bodies on the side of the road, ravaged and covered in layers of dust. The drug lord loses nothing, gains respect, and instills fear."

"What have I done, Maria? The white-haired grandmother who once blessed me, who brought me into the family's embrace now sits alone in the dark of her cave. The smoke inside grows thick and although it leaks out of the entrance, fresh air cannot make inroads. The bonfire consumes dozens of ears of dried blue corn, and the spirits of the slaughtered family fill the old woman's lungs. She suffocates on the souls of the dead. Too many crowd together in the hot smoke and seek refuge inside the grandmother's heart and blood, even as her organs shrivel and hiss in the crackle of the fire.

"............"

"It's too terrible Maria, I'm done. I'd better hang up now. I'm done."

"I give you permission to give up hope James, to give up on your calculations, your theories and false clues. To cease believing in miracles, in goodness, in recovery. Know that he is lost forever and that even if you disappear from this country James, you will not have slipped away from yourself. It is not possible. But now you can see that you still have your ear of dried blue corn James. Your infinite potential. Crush the single kernel, make the sign of the cross on your forehead, and begin again. Don't toss infinity into the fire, James. You must try to release yourself. Now I must change my oxygen tank."

"Goodbye Maria."

"Goodbye James. Call me tonight."

"........."

The End

Once upon a time Snow White rode to campus on a skateboard, her bra strap showing, sunglasses on. In mere moments she found herself pressing into a dark corner with Prince Charming. When his hands flattened on the brick wall behind him, Snow White saw the glint of his gold wedding band. But they were beyond that, the two of them. They were not creatures of the earth, not bound by the rules of gravity, of molecular composition, of matrimony. What could hold them down?

They were supremely connected, each allowed to probe into the other, to experience the brilliance of intimacy, the sheer power of falling into another person. And without articulation, without ruining everything with words, they maneuvered like private shadows in the dark corner. Snow White saw herself kneeling before Prince Charming, with his face unclear in her mind except his eyes. The color of Alaskan blue ice, the texture of a rose petal, round and perfect.

What could be said? The cosmos had smashed them together and so they sat next to one another at a séance. Body heat radiating from their thighs, exchanging themselves through their shared skin, and agitating their minds. They trembled for no reason and Snow White showed the other guests her quivering hand. The two of them existed in the presence of the impossible, the miraculous. On the way home after the party, traveling down a dark road, they pulled far off to the side. Nothing to say, how impossible to express. Snow White straddled the driver. Prince Charming's warm hands moved beneath her dress and up her body to communicate with her breasts. Heavy breath, sweet breath, fogged the windshield. Rain tapped all around and the front seat lowered back, as far back as it went. They were delivered unto one another.

So it happens that Snow White would not die from her desire to consume and be consumed by Prince Charming after all. The spell had broken and she sat in a bathtub of water turned cold. A coffee mug of urine sat in the sink with a pregnancy stick showing baby. In the garbage, three other sticks had shown baby as well. At that moment no little worker elves had ever existed nor any such bird that helped string up laundry on the clothesline. Prince Charming occurred to her as a simple man, not to say unattractive, but simply a man like any other. A slight headache accompanied that moment and her eyes burned. "The Fever," as she once called it, had run its course, presumably having burned up the contagion which she once called "Love." Even the episodes with Prince Charming seemed to dissipate into the air around Snow White's head. Becoming steam-like images clear enough in tone, but visually hopeless.

What's more, Snow White tried to believe that everything would still come up roses. She had finally descended from cloud nine and at that very moment, through the most remote regions of her complex being, Snow White moved on with her life. Decisions were being made, plans formulated, perhaps even, lessons learned about what she never called an "Affair." Snow White raised

both hands and felt her waterlogged fingertips press against
her face. Sadness treaded through her body, peaking like
labor pains in her chest, and yet she thought to herself, only
roses for me, only roses.

Then there was telekinetic hopeful, Prince
Charming. He sat at a wooden table across town eating
forkfuls of egg burrito with fresh tomato salsa. He drank
beer. More often than not he practiced moving the world
with imagined mental powers. With his eyes closed and a
quick flick of the wrist, he attempted to wave doors shut or
float beer bottles to his mouth. Precisely nothing happened.
He wanted to dissolve himself into particles of light and
pour into Snow White.
Not exactly your typical Prince Charming, he didn't
even have a horse.
He rode to town on a tiny stunt dirtbike, his
lowrider bicycle-- hands perched on handlebars at his eye
level. He wore a baseball cap backward. On a street corner
he gripped the handlebars and swung the bike around and
around beneath him, jumping over it like rope. He rode
onto campus tilted onto the rear tire. Prince Charming
stopped in front of the university library, locked his bike
and re-oriented the world to his height. He was five foot
six inches tall and for him, at that moment, everything was
Snow White.
The way information is anymore who knows what
really happened, but while reading in the library Prince
Charming suddenly had the impulse to see Snow White. A
usual enough occurrence considering their psychic
connection. While he gathered his books, Prince Charming
reviewed his situation as he had done so many times before.
He rented a house in a nice neighborhood with a brown-
haired young woman for whom he had certain feelings, a

woman whom his parents adored and to whom he had
often made love. Enough love so that he found himself in a
marriage ceremony not so long ago, enjoying each moment
and committing it to memory. But now he had a promising
career as a professional bicycle trickster, magician,
superhero,..and on and on. Everything seemed possible to
Prince Charming, especially being with Snow White, and
especially happily ever after.

But today when he stepped into the sunshine and
unlocked his bike to go see Snow White, the tone of the
world had suddenly changed. Instead, the sun shone like
florescent light, smacking off the sharp corners of his
bicycle, his hands felt sticky, and the air seemed
conditioned. Something was changing and he knew he must
ride immediately to her house. He put his hand to his
forehead, and felt only the barest warmth. He feared that
what they called their "Fever" was receding.

What were once called "gods," Snow White liked to
call "Readers" since all along it seemed they'd scanned her
life for imperfections, for character flaws that would
inevitably lead to her spectacular demise, her narrative
unraveling like a failed rocket launch.

And if the Readers had heard any of this out loud
they might appear and look her straight in the eyes and say,
"What? You do some guy in a car, get pregnant and that's
it?" Which is not enough for the Readers, and which is
precisely the reason Snow White had been crying for so
long in the tub. She couldn't make them understand
because they were only interested in details, and those
disappear. She grew furious and asked herself, how did you
expect it to turn out? "Love" could not keep it together.

Snow White's illusion, her elaborate fiction. After
all, cars don't really transform into giant search engines of
the soul. Clouds don't descend from the sky to cushion two
people virtually levitating inside the car. Now crawling into
the backseat, now ripping through pantyhose, now rocking.

Snow White put her hand on the hot water nozzle,
cold metal. She turned it on and water fell, more or less
warm at first. Then cold, only cold. The well outside the
cottage was not the deepest so a Reader might think that
she would've turned off the water when it started to
overflow. Instead, water moved over the side of the tub in
small waves, forming puddles on the floor.

"Are you going to keep the baby? Do you have
health insurance? Aren't you a little young to be a mother?
Babies need plenty of attention."

Prince Charming's wife, a sweet woman indeed,
who had for so long remained beside the point, had
instantly become the only point left. Which for Snow
White made the situation all the more tragic.
Snow White had fallen, had become the 'other woman.'
But they had existed beyond all that, hadn't they? beyond all
of those gritty normal terms and phrases.
They had dwelt in a castle, souls at play, in fusion. So he
must never know about the baby, he must never learn how
many times Snow White will have to get up at night to feed
the baby, or to soothe the baby. Instead, they have been
extinguished, and that was that.

Snow White: pale white skin, watermelon colored
lips, black hair spilling out of the bathtub. Her bathroom
floor spreads with water, leaks under the door into the
hallway. It'll be into the living room carpet within minutes,
the dark orange color darkening, soaking like a sponge. In
this way though, she knows she could never drown. She
would have to slip under or knock her head against the side
of the tub and sink to the bottom.

Prince Charming rode up the bike path into the mountains. His mind recalled events of the week as if gathering evidence, trying to prop up his world, trying to focus on the good times. But they blurred almost beyond recollection. Episodes that once carried tremendous weight, that were clear evidence of "True Love," melted as he sweat on his mini-bike. He wondered in a panic if this Snow White existence was somehow genetically engineered to fail. He pedaled through the dissolving fog of her skin, and touch and smell. Soon, he could not even recall Snow White's face.

As he strained to re-ignite his feelings for Snow White, the events from the past week suddenly presented themselves as omens, as warning signs that had clearly foretold of this doom. The end, (what an idiot he'd been!), had been especially obvious just the day before, during his intramural softball game. A ball had been hit high and Prince Charming backpedaled. Even though he played short stop he moved back, deep into center field shading the sun with his glove.
"I got it, I got it," he shouted. The ball landed firmly in his mitt with a satisfying smack. The girl who actually played center field looked at him with a hand on her hip and said, "Nice work, Bully." Better safe than sorry he thought but when he threw the ball to the pitcher he saw the umpire holding a red handkerchief in the air. Prince Charming was called for male dominance and the batter was allowed to trot to second base. Who ever heard of male dominance in softball?

Yes, it was coming clearer to Prince Charming and terror tickled his body. The momentum of his life shifted and he knew soon that Snow White would disappear and he

would no longer attempt to move the world with his mind.
He left his bike by the creek and ran up the path to the
small house. He was frantic by the time he pounded on the
door. How could it end like this? What could he possibly
say?

Words were a dilemma for Snow White at that
moment as well. Her lips had gone numb. Such a trap,
such a vulgar and impossible web of meaning to navigate if
you wanted to tell about how it was, if you wanted to
expose their beauty together. Always when she looked at
Prince Charming it was as if his skin melted around the
edges, as if they were actually enchanted, floating.

It's all about metaphor, she thought. Their whole
romance boiled down to a goddamn metaphor, lived in
virtual spaces, with fantastic notions. How terrible it felt to
recover, how wretched. Too bad mental telepathy failed,
she thought caustically and shook her head. What kind of
ridiculous illness could've made them believe that they were
capable of speaking into each other's brain, of breathing
from inside the other's skin?

Snow White used to organize her day around Prince
Charming. She would calculate distance and time in order
for them to meet and walk together. She would kick the
skateboard into her hand and walk beside him. Together
they felt like a fountain, nourishing and whole. The water
from the faucet had turned a rusted red color and spread in
the bathtub like clouds of Easter-egg coloring, definitely
draining the bottom of the well. Maybe three inches of
water sat on the bathroom floor, less in the rest of the small
house.

Grape soda pop did not come out of the faucet.
There were exactly zero magic queens or talking lions in this
scene. No one cast a spell on anyone else and magic potion
saved exactly no one. It seemed to Snow White that kissing
would do about as much.

Prince Charming had never broken down a door in his life so he walked around the cabin looking for a window to open, or if necessary, to break with a rock. When he came to the bathroom window he looked down and saw Snow White lying in the tub with her head tilted back, eyes closed. Her cheeks and lips had seemingly drained into the blood colored water. He ran to the front door and tried the knob again, still locked. This is real, he told himself. He rested his forehead against the door and thought, this is real, I should do something.

Snow White was freezing by then and decided to stand. Liquid trickled from the faucet, pure rust by now. She wrapped a towel around her body and walked through the water into the bedroom to lie on her bed. She closed the door. It was clear to her by now that Prince Charming had vanished.

Prince Charming removed a screen and lifted the front window. He went in head first, and let himself down gently onto the couch.

One night, Prince Charming had bitten Snow White's neck on this couch. The memory of this, of his desire to taste her blood, receded like sound and he couldn't exactly recall what had made him want to do that. In fact, it didn't make any sense at all. He felt his head screw on straight and he knew that there was precisely nothing vampiric in his body anymore. Even the flavor dissolved and he remembered it like flowers. Since when does blood taste like flowers? Who could he ever tell this to?

He walked on the soaking carpet, trying to be as quiet as possible. All of the doors were closed except the bathroom and he looked in. Someone had taken the body. He stood next to the bathtub and water soaked through the bottom of his shoes, into his socks. Her clothes were wet rags in the corner and he picked them up, lifted them to his face, and dropped them in a pile at his feet. When he glanced at the sink, he saw the coffee cup of urine with the pregnancy stick showing baby, and it was clear to him that Snow White had disappeared.

Behind him, she cleared her throat. "Excuse me," she said, "are you looking for someone?" She stood in her doorway, a gray towel wrapped up around her breasts, arms crossed. Hair wet and tangled.

This woman's eyes were red and her skin had wrinkled into that of an old woman.   No symphony struck up. No musical interlude, no lovers embracing and grooming each other like saved souls. Nothing but drips into the tub.

"No," he said. "No. They must have taken her away."

She shrugged.

No last kiss. Only the sounds of his sloshing footsteps and the closing of the front door.

Metawriter

Who is still at the Detroit car show waiting to see what's inside the cardboard box under the table? Many will have declared the entire event to be a gimmick, a marketing ploy, the intention of which may still be unclear, but their irritation is not. Others have become engaged in conversation about entirely different topics, some have left and are already on their way home. The few who remain at the convention center, some of whom are too drunk to leave, stare at the stage. I crouch down, slide the box out from under the table and open the top. I reach in and pick up a human head, my head. Someone laughs; a man faints and a woman gasps. The mouth of the head is moving even as I hold it like a basketball under one arm. The words coming out sound like this:

The writer's role also does not escape the effects of metafiction. With storytelling exposed to some degree the writer's process is unveiled for what it is, a series of deliberate choices. This understanding seems at first to undermine the writer's credibility since that credibility used to come from the writer's ability to construct what John Gardner refers to the vivid and continuous dream of the narrative. But before the metafiction writer can be dismissed as a self-indulgent experimenter, the consequences of the various exposures must be examined. By highlighting the process in each aspect of fiction, from the reader, to the character, to the plot, the writer underscores one of metafiction's favorite themes, that both fiction and reality are constructions.

Patricia Waugh defends metafiction when she says:

> Metafiction, then, does not abandon 'the real world' for the narcissistic pleasure of the imagination. What it does is to re-examine the conventions of realism in order to discover—through its own self-reflection—a fictional form that is culturally relevant and comprehensible to contemporary readers. In showing us how literary fiction creates its imaginary worlds, metafiction helps us to understand how the reality we   live day by day is similarly constructed, similarly 'written'. (Waugh 36)

But just because they are constructions is not to say then that they do not have value. This judgment is leftover from the days when fact's supremacy was widely recognized and fiction was regarded simply as entertainment or play. Quite the contrary, the idea that reality is a constructed implies that it is made up of both fact and fiction. Reality is a compilation of both, a fusion of those bits of information which were once so decidedly labeled and categorized.

The metafiction writer is in essence mapping out a process by which we knowingly assimilate and construct our realities. Just as the traditional writer once viewed fiction as the exploration of psychological human behavior, the metafiction writer views fiction as the exploration of the way we go about making and presenting reality. The imagination consciousness is the name of this process.

The hyper-awareness of the individual can be seen in the sudden interest in the issue of bias with regards to journalism. Suddenly we are all very aware of the sources from which our information comes and we are adjusting the information as we receive it. The consciousness part of the

imagination consciousness is a gesture to this hyper-
awareness, this freeing of the consciousness from the boxes
into which we once funneled our experiences. The fluid
consciousness records and collects, and is more at ease with
being unstable and unhinged.

But if we are becoming hyperaware and we no
longer have the traditional boxes, how do we deal with the
sheer volume of information that we receive? The
imagination is particularly suited to this task. Once a term
used to designate the creative abilities of an artist or
inventor or philosopher, the imagination has been
democratized. Evidence of this can be seen in the
explosion of creative writing programs throughout the
country. People recognize the impulse to do something
with this accumulation of fact and fiction. The imagination
is designed to unite disparate pieces and it is this act that
leads to coherence and ultimately meaning.

The imagination consciousness is a term designed to
reflect the consequence of the metafictive impulse. The
exposure of past rules and systems and the emphasis on
process has indeed led to the investigation of the line
between fiction and reality. But it would be impossible to
proclaim that the consequences of that investigation resided
solely in the realm of fiction. Of course reality must be
affected as well, and as such we see the imagination
consciousness flourish as individuals collect process and
assemble meaning from the bits of fact and truth and rumor
and memory and half-truths and recollections and that story
they read from where they can't remember, and on and on.

At this point you've almost finished reading this
critical essay and may be in a position to judge whether or
not I have succeeded in my attempt to introduce and define
a new literary term. Ultimately, the success of the term
'imagination consciousness' relies on you; your willingness

to adopt this term relies not only on its own merit but also on your current state of mind, your mood. Perhaps it would be better to put this essay aside and come back to it later when you're more favorably disposed to the possibility of a new literary term. It would be a pity for the 'imagination consciousness' to suffer the same fate as 'postmortemism,' another term which I attempted to launch many years ago. At this point however, the fate of this term is out of my hands. I have done my bit, played my role. It's time for me to put my head back inside the box.

Works Cited

Baxter, Charles. Burning Down The House. Minnesota:
Graywolf, 1998.

Barth, John. Lost in the Funhouse. New York: Anchor,
1988.

Barthelme, Donald. "At the End of the Mechanical Age."
Hemley 15-21.

Bellipanni, Jason. "Out of Your Mind." Short Story.

Calvino, Italo. Cosmicomics. Trans. William Weaver.
New York: Harcourt, 1968.
---. If on a winter's night a traveler. Trans. William
Weaver. New York: Harcourt,   1981.
---. Mr. Palomar. Trans. William Weaver. New York:
Harcourt, 1985.
---. Six Memos for the Next Millennium. Trans. Patrick
Creagh. Cambridge: Harvard Press, 1988.

Dixon, Stephen. "Milk Is Very Good For You." Hemley
165-175.

"For The Record: Bush Documents." CBSNEWS.com. 20
Sep. 2004 <http://www.cbsnews.com/stories/2004/09
/15/60II/printable 643768.shtml.>.

Gardner, John. The Art of Fiction. New York: Vintage,
1991.
Grow, Jennifer. "All that is seen and unseen: Negative
Space in Fiction." Chronicle. December 2003. 1 Jan. 2005
<http://elink.awpwriter.org/m/awpChron/articles/
         jgrow01. lasso>.

Hawkes, John. "Life And Art: An Interview With John

Hawkes." Dalkey Archive Press.   2 Jan 2005
http://centerforbookculture.org/interviews/interview_haw
kes.html>.

Hembree, R.J. "The ABCs of Reality Construction."
Writers' Village University. 1 Jan   2005
http://www.writopia.org/preview/Metafiction.htm

Hemley, Robin and Martone, Michael, eds. Extreme
Fiction: Fabulists and Formalists.   New York: Pearson
2004.

Maso, Carole. "An Interview with Carole Maso." Dalkey
Archive Press. 2 Jan 2005
        <http://centerforbookculture.org/interviews/interv
iew_maso.html>.

"Metafiction." Wikipedia: The Free Online Encyclopedia.
27 Feb 2005
        <http://en.wikipedia.org/wiki/Metafiction>.

Paley, Grace. "A Conversation With My Father." Hemley
26-30.

Saramago, Jose. All the Names. Trans. Margaret Jull Costa.
New York: Harcourt, 1999. ---. Blindness. Trans. Juan
Sager. New York: Harcourt, 1999.
---. The Cave. Trans. Margaret Jull Costa. New York:
Harcourt, 2003.

Shafer, Jack. "The Jayson Blair Project." Slate. 8 May 2003
<http://slate.msn.com/toolBar.aspx?action=print&id=208
2741>.

Waugh, Patricia. Metafiction: The Theory and Practice of Self-Conscious Fiction. New York: Routledge/ Taylor & Francis e-library, 2001.

Words Fail

In my study I put my index finger on the floor and then my body floats up, sometimes spins around. This is my answer to the, 'are you in touch with reality' question. Meaning, I am touching it, what else do you expect?

Words fail, of course. In the car I drive and speak to my wife, sitting beside me. We drive in a bathtub it seems, a shower scene because when we stop at a light and I turn to the car next to me, the gentleman looks like, hey man I'm a little busy in my shower here. So I look ahead. All of this intimacy and so I say certain words in order to communicate my good will toward her, my affection.

She responds in accordance, also making familiar sounds, forming words that have lost meaning. As if to say, right back at you. Love.And we drive on.So I begin to look instead for secret signals, gestures that I hope can communicate something true, not warped or distorted by hollow words that can no longer be filled up. When we were young I wanted to make up a new word for love, a way to break with the past, since we'd both already used it enough. God knows. And then I thought, why not a new language altogether, our own secret code. But after one usage the words fell like cellophane smeared with mayonnaise.

Gave up on language, so it was obvious the next step. Physical signals, what has been termed body language. But the gestures that resemble the familiar have lost meaning, only the secret ones, the unconscious ones matter. You can take those to the bank, or so I thought.

Let us say that she has a laugh, a certain laugh that you are able to withdraw from her, as if with a special trick of the hands, a magic manipulation of the wrist. A note of shock, if you were forced to describe it, a delight in that sound that transmits the knowledge that you have a place inside her body. Somewhere in there, you dwell, you matter and effect. A joyful noise which you alone can elicit, it is a hook into her, a grounding of sorts which maybe count as connection.

And so we say that you hear that laugh, as if a moment had opened up, a hollow in time from which this sound rises and strikes you. In your study you've been busy, distracted, one finger touching the ground, your feet treading on the ceiling. An open book in one hand and you read. But then you hear it, the laugh, and she talks on the phone to an old friend. Your body falls as it does on occasion, a balance has been upset perhaps and with your skin pressing into the floor perhaps you sense the motion of the earth on its axis. Perhaps you don't. In any event you wait.

Do you hear it again, or at least believe that you do? One more time, the sound scurries like so many microscopic mice and under your door and into your ear canals. And you itch because of it. Because of the secret signal, which was not a secret signal after all. It was only a normal signal, a noise that she, as a creature, makes with her vocal chords in response to some stimuli. A regular noise like,

"I love you too." Empty for you, and you reel in that hook, which you see was not a hook at all, but more like a lead ball bearing that you must have heaved into her at one point and then forgotten about. Mistaken for a hook after time had passed, when really it just sat in there, sloshing around. You were tricking yourself again you silly goat. Tricks are for rabbits.

But you've heard it twice now, no? Breaking the plane of your concentration. You might not have even noticed it at all; perhaps it would have been better this way. Believing in the hook, in the connection, but you are forced to reel it in under the door and think yourself a silly man for behaving this way, for concerning yourself over the sound from a young woman, whom you amorviate, as you once called it.

Let us not stop there. Let us also say that there is a peculiar look, an arrangement of her facial muscles, completely involuntary, unconscious and so not tainted by plans and intent. A look of adoration you might say, angelic as if in the portraits of the Madonna which you have seen. Holy and beatific that you orchestrate into existence, not unlike a conductor. A secret recipe that you yourself could not write down, which means of course that it is real, that it signifies.

You maneuver based on intuition, based on direction provided by impulse and the gods. As if you stood over a caldron on the correct day of the year and stirred with a broken broom handle and happen to look into the pot at precisely the right moment and there it is, her look, the facial muscles stretching the skin in order to show this, this connection you have. This numb mastery over the workings of her blood, and hormonal release. You could not detail it, who could? but you know it and you have seen it appear over the table as you cracked a lobster claw and she held a glass of wine in her hand.

Sure you must often use generic words in the dance of elicitation, fabricated gestures, planned revelation of sentiment. You dance on the court, elbowing what you must, dodging and spinning and then pulling and there it is, coaxed into existence, your reward, your certification. You dwell in her, how else can it be?

And so it appears, the look, slowly coming over her face, not unlike a weather pattern, but you have done no work at all. You sit side by side, and you think as you watch her that perhaps you've grown so expert at the process you can make the look appear just by the pulsing of your blood, through the invisible transmissions of you body heat. But you see that she watches television as she sits next to you and does horror excite your blood? She does not look at you, but at the images, the millions of electrical impulses that make up pictures, that then fabricate drama. And her look is aimed there, at the screen, at the appliance and you do not move for fear of dissolution. A television drama has pulled the look from her, that same look, of this you are certain, more certain that you care to be.

Do you make a list? Do you write down every possible physical signal, every indication that the two of you dwell in one another? Can it be that there is no such thing as dwelling, as hooking into souls, as connecting? But words have already failed, you plead in your study. At least there is this, right? RIGHT?

And do you take out that list every so often and cross off another gesture? A list that already contains phrases and words which you have had to abandon by now. A notebook, really, with pages full of words crossed out. One by one they fall, the gestures, the secret signals, until at dinner you sit over a piece of cooked chicken. Why don't new signals arise to replace the old? Can it be that the infinite pool of gestures has by now, been exhausted, emptied and infected. Only silence reigns now and it has a difficult time confirming anything.

"We never talk anymore," she says. And the sounds of the words, the way in which she holds her fork, they are like lightning flashes and you cannot look, you must close your ears to the thunder.

"I love you," you retaliate. And already you can see through your hand, your arm. Rising out of your seat like a helium balloon. You think, I am connected to nothing.

"I love you too," she says and then she displays what used to be the look, she puts it on her face like make-up. Obviously you must be a television show, you must be a fabricated bit of drama. Put together with blocks of meaning, sewn together with proven ways to elicit emotion. No anchors at all now and your head bangs on the ceiling but she does not notice or does not comment. What could she say after all?

The Story of My Success by Carl Diffenrocket,

(Automotive and household appliance swallower of the year 2002,2004,2007)

Rest assured I'm cranking out the insights even as you read this; I've put together a contraption using an old bathtub, a broken lawn mower, and several pieces of rotted two by fours. Turn the crank on one end and a somewhat nicely wrapped tin foil package falls out the front. Insight. And of course, like a good aspiring writer, my job is to tape it onto my stories. If I can figure out a way to add calcium, I'm sure my work would sell.

This story has visited slush piles all around the world.

My baby boy falls asleep in a peculiar way, he tosses his head from side to side, really whacks his cheek against my leg, or else his crib mattress. Trying to latch onto sleep. And it strikes me how much like life this really is, how true an action my child is performing. I pick him up and push him into the machine. Bing, insight anyone?

Some people nod at me and they say, yes, yes this is precisely how it is, trying to latch onto sleep, trying to connect with that super darkness, that blackness of gravity that pulls our consciousness down until we drool. These people say that I must be an insightful writer, which is good, because stories in magazines are supposed to contain insight; I should be in good shape.

In the beginning I calculated how many stories I would need to write per month in order to make a living, and then I set off. Multiple rejection syndrome followed with all of the usual results. If you're like me then you've heard it a million times. The writer saves rejections in shoebox, moves forward, and struggles with all the delusional energy of an actual idiot. If only I'd had the machine back then.

I walked down Main Street one afternoon dressed like a bum. Details like torn flannel shirt, scraggly brown beard, curly brown hair (unkempt), cigarette in my mouth. I squinted into my palm and wrote in a small notepad.

A tuxedoed fat man with a gray goatee and a top hat strolled to a stop; a buxom young woman hung on his arm. He gripped the hook of a polished mahogany cane and looked me over. The woman could have been, but clearly was not, his daughter. A diamond tiara glittered on her ocean of blond hair. An emerald choker necklace attached her head to her body. She wore an ivory Cinderella ball gown, fringed with lace.

"I say," the man said. "What have we here? My, my, a real struggling writer—a live one indeed." He lifted his cane and prodded my side with the fat rubber tip.

The woman stiffened, smiled, and pulled herself closer to her father-like date.

The man reached into his breast pocket and withdrew a wad of cash; he peeled away a single dollar bill and held it pinched in between his fat thumb and forefinger. "You there," he called to me. "I say, my good man—do me a favor and struggle a little for the lady."

"Honestly, Harold," the woman said.

He looked at her and stroked her hand. He stared at her, a little too long, and said, "Isn't she precious?" He turned and aimed his shiny black stare at me. "What do you say to a little struggle on this fine day?" He waved the dollar bill. I could have lunged forward and grabbed it with my teeth.

His date watched me intently; her eyes widened, her red lips parted, her choker bobbed once when she swallowed. "Do you think he's drunk?" she asked in a false whisper.

"Come now my good man, that's the way," the man said and he bent a little at the knee, dangling the money off to the side, showing me, persuading me.

I collapsed onto the ground. I rolled on the sidewalk with my tongue out of my mouth. I groaned and gagged and spit onto my chin. I flailed onto the street and my legs slammed against a parked car. I growled at the air and pretended to weep. It actually felt good, this writhing, this fake crying: a physical performance of my inner turmoil. Real pain, instead of blurry anxiety. I scraped my chin squirming back onto the cement.

I barely heard them laughing as they walked away.

But the struggle didn't end; after a while, I rolled over and picked up the money. My first writing-related dollar. I sat for a long time against a building with the dollar crushed in my hand. My body shuddered while I watched the people pass by.

I saw my notepad under a parked car. It must have slid out during my fit. I decided to retrieve it after I'd composed myself, after I'd regained control.

While I waited, the crying went on and on.

Nice writing here, some clarity would probably help this get published.

Though I haven't the tactile sensation, I have snuggled up with hundreds of other writers in editor's piles all across the country. Coffee stains, dog drool, hours of mindless babble, all co-habitating for a while in the pile being readied to be shipped back home.

I thought at first that I had been called by God, and so having been thusly chosen my effort would simply require to allow the Great One access to my puny mind, the skills of my opposable thumbs. And so I did, I streamed out a bunch of words, lumped into stories and then sent them off. I ended up working in a restaurant. My wife said I should be patient, that it could take years. And I remember thinking tenderly, how the hell would she know?

The more I learn about words, the more they fail. In the car I drive and speak to my wife, sitting beside me. We drive in a bathtub it seems, a shower scene because when we stop at a light and I turn to the car next to me, the gentleman looks at me like, *hey man I'm a little busy in my shower here.* So I look ahead. All of this intimacy and so I say certain words in order to communicate my good will toward my wife, remind her of my affection.

She responds in accordance, also making familiar sounds, forming words that have lost meaning. As if to say, right back at you. Love.

And we drive on.

To avoid disappointment I begin to look instead for secret signals, gestures that I hope can communicate something true, not warped or distorted by hollow words that can no longer be filled up. When we were young I wanted to make up a new word for love, a way to break with the past, since we'd both already used it enough. God knows. And then I thought, why not a new language altogether, our own secret code. But after one usage the words fell like cellophane smeared with mayonnaise.

Let us say that my wife had a peculiar look, an arrangement of her facial muscles, completely involuntary, unconscious and so not tainted by plans and intent. A look of adoration, holy and beatific, that I orchestrate into existence, not unlike a conductor. A secret recipe that I could not write down, which means of course that it is real, that it signifies. I maneuver based on intuition, based on direction provided by impulse and the gods. As if I stood over a caldron on the correct day of the year and stirred with a broken broom handle and happened to look into the pot at precisely the right moment and there it would be, her look, the facial muscles stretching the skin in order to show this connection that we have. It is a numb mastery over the workings of her blood, an invisible control over her hormonal release. I could not detail it, who could? But I know it and I have seen it appear over the table as I cracked a lobster claw and she held a glass of wine in her hand.

Of course I must often use generic words in the dance of elicitation, fabricated gestures, planned revelation of sentiment. I dance on the court, boxing out potential distraction, dodging and spinning and then pulling and there it is, coaxed into existence, my reward, my certification. I dwell in her, how else can it be?

And so it appears, the look, slowly coming over her face, not unlike a weather pattern, but I have done no work at all. We sit side by side, and as I watch her I consider the idea that perhaps I've grown so expert at the process that I can make the look appear just by the pulsing of my blood, through the invisible transmissions of my body heat.

But I see that she watches television as she sits next to my and horror excites my blood. She does not look at me, but at the images, the millions of electrical impulses that make up pictures and fabricate drama. And her look is aimed there, at the screen, at the appliance and I do not move for fear of dissolution. A television drama has pulled the look from her, that same look; of this I am more certain that I care to be.

The next night at dinner she says, "We never talk anymore." And the sounds of the words, the way in which she holds her fork, they are like lightning flashes and I cannot look, I must close my ears to the thunder.

"I love you," I retaliate. And already I can see through my hand, my arm. I rise out of my seat like a helium balloon. I think, *I am connected to nothing.*

"I love you too," she says and then she displays what used to be the look, she puts it on her face like make-up. Obviously I must be a television show; I must be a fabricated bit of drama—put together with blocks of meaning, sewn together with proven ways to elicit emotion. No anchors at all now and my head bangs on the ceiling but she does not notice or does not comment. What could she say after all?

Where's the story? No plot here.

By now this story has been sent back to me 23 times.

Books about writing are like chocolate cakes. Sometimes you've just got to have one, and after you eat the entire thing you may want to vomit into the trash bin, but find that you cannot. The magic assimilating chocolate cake. I look past the writing. I develop my wild mind. I set up a writing schedule, I read good books and bad books, I alternately care and don't care about the type of pen I'm using. I try to entertain and then shun entertainment in favor of depth and confusion. I learn about art and serious fiction and then I read a serious published story in a serious magazine. It is chock full of insight, and I find that I can vomit. Hurrah for insight.

Here's a cohesive narrative structure.

I read, "...*the editors regret to inform you......*" and then I think, "I have been rejected by places ten times better than you buddy." And so they do not get put into the shoebox labeled *TRY AGAIN I*. Oh no, it is straight into the shoebox labeled *TRY AGAIN II* for those pompous bastards.

I read stories about impossibly famous writers and their disastrous beginnings. I count my rejection slips, and until it got out of hand I used to organize them from best to worst. Somehow now, it is all the same. But the cohesive narrative point is that I begin to believe that despite my continual failure, I am one of those up and coming famous authors. Rejection only solidifies my status. Even as I write in my journals, which have become numerous, I write as though someone will be reading my words in years to come. I look at posterity and try to get it right for them, so that when they go through my journals and sell each one for thousands of dollars I will have accurately detailed my tortuous journey.

Even now as this story sits in a slush pile, I must wonder who I am writing to. But it is to You, of course, the ever emerging You who waits for me though you do not know it. Just then another associate editor slipped this story in the return envelope and went on with the day's business. Listen up—

My grandfather said: "For dinner you must eat as many fresh clams as possible. You must have scrubbed them thoroughly and left them in salted water overnight, maybe two nights. You must wipe them down so that they appear as polished gray stones, perfectly symmetrical, and containing what you need. Steam them in some white wine, some stock, in a giant pot. Pick through them, burning the tips of your fingers and removing the solid ones, the heavy ones feel loaded down with sand, they are dead. You work on this for two days maybe into a third and you make pasta on Christmas Eve for the calms to lie upon. You pluck out the still warm flesh and toss them with olive oil, sprinkle with chopped parsley.

"You must do this so when, with the spaghetti wound tight and with the clam resting like an infant between the folds, fleeting, you will see the grain of sand. But only as your mouth closes down on the fork, lips tight as you pull away leaving the warm food in your mouth, only then does it register what you saw and when you chew, and when your tooth comes down on that rock granule that the ocean has not completely dissolved over the past few centuries, then you are ready to grow up and grow old. All of your preparation can not stop the forces beyond your control, all of your intense concentration on how things ought to be, on what you want, erased in a flash, by the gritty sand scratching your tooth and sending a shudder down your back.

You have learned not to expect satisfaction, and so you are closer to your grandfather during that bowl of pasta than ever before in your life. Finish eating and drinking, you have also learned that there are more moments to come."

I promised myself at one point that at the very least I would never write about being a writer. How absolutely dull and banal would that be? Bing!

Guy goes to writing program and meets beautiful woman who works at a restaurant. Her name is Beth. She does not talk about point of view or character development and he sort of wants to eat her because of it. But this guy is already married. Do you see the tension? Could it be any more obvious? Well he sneaks around on his wife in the interests of art, of course, in the interests of pursuing emotion over reason. His wife finds out, and does she forgive him? Hell no, she's outta there like a flash of light. The man is sad and poetically wonders what it could all mean, and the story ends with a barely enigmatic line like, "Then he took off his shoes for the last time."

Like he went barefoot from then on, became Jesus of Nazareth. Something.

A year later, Ike calls me one day, eating.

He says, "Hey man you got any stories for me?"

At first I think he's tearing into a bag of chips. And then I think he's pulling off strips of fruit roll-up. "How's it going?"

"Shitty," he says. "I'm stuck in this cabin supposed to be making masterpieces and everything turns into masturbation. You?"

"Good." I hear the sound of fabric tearing and his mouth sounds full. "What the hell are you eating, a pillow?"

The words, "my chair," barely audible beneath the muffled sounds. His chewing continues and he finally swallows which makes me want a drink. "Yeah, it's one of those office ones with a padded butt and back. Blue fabric, white fluffy stuffing." Another rip and another mouthful. "Got stories?"

I'm trying to understand Ike. Trying to decide if he's called who he thinks he's called because I haven't written anything in almost a year. I'm not convinced that he knows who I am. "How's the art going?"

"Shhhuty." Then he either swallows or else shoves the fabric into his cheek like a ball player and talks. "It's hell up here Jake. Fire all summer, snow all winter. You should see the black trees all over the goddamn place. The animals were smart to get the hell out. It's like a time warp, a fast forward version of evolution." He continues to chew. "I've already swallowed eleven screws, the easy ones."

I feel like I should somehow already know, but I ask, "Why are you eating your chair? Do you need money?"

"I don't need money Jake," he says and then begins to cough. I wait until he's cleared his throat. "I need stories Jake, some goddamn honest to goodness art. I also need a new chair."

"I haven't done anything for a while Ike."
"Did you burn everything like every good genius does?"
"No. It's sitting right here." He probably didn't even know that I had a job and a life, of sorts. I was a software tester for a computer company, and I wasn't sure if I would tell him this or not. No one wants to say they've failed.

I heard more fabric tear and then a loud thump. "Fell over," he said and I assumed he meant the chair. "Send what you got," he said. "Need story," he said as if he were drowning.

"How's Beth," I ask. Maybe she would arrive in time to stop him from eating the metal ball bearings.

"Good," he says and I hear him hitting something. "Well, not so good. I'm training to eat a car, of course, and she doesn't think it's the greatest idea. She's still a waitress up here in god forsaken land. This plastic is a mother to swallow."

"Well, I could send you the charging ram story. If you want."

"I sit in this cabin Jake and I stare out the one window and I can't figure out what the hell I'm doing. Then I look down at the plywood and paint in front of me and remember, I'm not doing a goddamn thing. Oh yeah, you ever sleep with Beth?"

He chews now in a different way, like he's got a large piece of gum in his cheek. He makes sucking sounds, trying to keep saliva in his mouth. I look at my own office chair and try to picture it in fragments, inside a stomach. I have the idea that a sharp edge could puncture the whole scenario without much trouble.

"Sure I slept with her," I said. "But that was before you guys were going out. What's my story going to do for you anyway? You going to eat it?"

But Ike didn't laugh, instead I heard the sounds of a small saw working through plastic and in went another piece. "Sometimes I think she might've been happier with you, you know? She comes home now, all distant and depressed. Of course I wonder if it's because I suck. I mean I haven't sculpted a goddamn thing in months, and nothing salable in my life. So I take up eating things. I tell her I'm going to make it into the Guinness book of world records. There's endorsement money in that. Eating a car has been done of course, that's just part of the training. You have to build up to it. I'm looking at a semi or maybe an old space shuttle. Or maybe a fleet of cars, like all brands of Ford or something like that."

"And the story?"

"Jesus do I have to spell it out. It's for inspiration Jake, it's so I can surround myself with creative shit, remind myself that what I'm doing is making art and not just fucking around. I need more relationship in my life."

Beth was a beautiful girl. Young, maybe immature, but smart and tough. She wasn't the type of girl who wanted to be cuddled and who hoped to settle down. She wanted adventure. Motorcycle rides at night without headlights, tattoos, piercings, cliff diving. Together, we were adventure for a while, but not because we did any of those things. Mainly because I was legally unavailable, my love spoken for, and I think she liked the feeling of stealing it. It was a game for her, even when the flashlight came through the car windshield and Beth hoped it was the cops and I already knew that it was Emily. Beth saw everything as a challenge, an adventure. I remember when she kissed me on the cheek and told me good luck behind the restaurant one night. It was such an excellent movie scene, her expression like take care kid, be good, it was real.

"These wheels are a bitch, man I'll have to smash them to bits just to get them to go down."

And so I began to think that I obviously never knew Ike at all, and apparently he never really knew me either. I mean I couldn't have been further away from writing when he called. I guess it's what happens when you don't keep in touch.

"You should tell Beth to pay me a visit," I say. "You know I'm a lonely bachelor now." I was being funny, sort of.

Ike stopped chewing. "I thought you had a kid."

"A kid and a divorce in the space of three years," I say. "Talk about the Guinness book. Anyway, what do you want a relationship with a story for, when you've got her."

Ike sighed which sounded more like a gurgle. "You don't have relationships with people Jake. Look, I have a relationship with this tee-shirt I'm wearing. You know why? Because I wash it in a tub with my own two hands, then I wring the hell out of it, and then I hang it over a lampshade to dry. You get to know things that way, and I mean actual things. They don't go and turn into a brick overnight, or a mountain lion. But you don't ever wring out a person. You don't know what's in there."

"Seems like I wrung the hell out of my marriage."

"And that's what you're left with, a whole lotta nothing. Animating the inanimate, that's the way to go. You said you're not writing anymore?"

"I test software."

"For what, herpes?"

"To see if it works, how easy it is to use, the usual. Did Beth ever get that tattoo of an apple around her belly button? I told her to go for it, but I wonder if she did. It was supposed to be the top of an apple, you know, with her belly button being the stem. Only it would be an emerald ring instead. I've thought about that."

"'That's' exactly what I mean. She's a character to you, hell she's a character to me. We're all a bunch of characters, walking around making guesses about everyone else. Now when you wash dishes, it's the same thing. You see the familiar blue plate, you touch the chip, wonder if it's getting bigger, wonder where the hell you got the plate in the first place. This is life experience, Jake, not touching people." He stopped to insert another piece of something in his mouth. "Do you see your kid?"

"Sometimes. I mean it's not a regular deal at all, no weekends or every other Wednesday, nothing like that. Just once in a while. Is Beth there, why don't you put her on while you go smash those wheels?"

"No, she's out."

"You've been watching television," I said. I knew this because the story had made the rounds about a guy eating his Ford explorer. He was doing commercials for Ford now, about how he would never have eaten any other brand of car. They show various x-rays of his stomach. I really want to talk to Beth.

"Of course I've been watching television, how else do you think I got in this mess? I'll tell you about TV." I couldn't stop thinking about her, and hoped that she would take the phone and start talking to me, but instead Ike drank some liquid, maybe Pennzoil and kept talking. "We all grew up watching this crap and so we developed this little part of our brain, this little filter. When we were kids and we saw some guy fall off a building and land on the cement the filter kicked in and whispered, 'Don't worry little guy, it's all pretend.' And so we grow up with this little voice and soon I'm watching bodies being pulled out of a crumbled building and my filter keeps on saying, 'Don't worry.' Nothing is real now and even when I try to convince myself, I'm no match for that practiced voice. Even when I say to myself, 'Dude this *is* real' I get nowhere, feel nothing."

Then he made the sounds like he was gagging and choking, and I heard a loud thunk which I guessed was the phone falling on the floor. And I thought that most people probably underrate the danger of eating furniture and cars and all that. Especially people like Ike. They probably don't even think about the possibility of choking to death. And I'd bet that Ike hadn't even given it any thought at all.

And while I waited for him to pick up the receiver, I secretly hoped that Beth would come back to me if things went bad with Ike. We would be perfect together, and I began to fantasize about how I'd cook her dinner, and how great it would be to be free with her. To spend time without the sensation that I had to keep looking over my shoulder. She would get comfortable on the couch with a glass of wine, her legs crossed beneath her black skirt and I'd sit next to her, brush her cheek with my hand. Maybe I'd talk about fate. Maybe I'd even propose marriage. That would be exciting. And by the time I had taken her glass of wine and made love to her on the couch, swirling my tongue around her belly button, pretending to eat the apple, I realized that the line had gone dead.

Eventually I hung up the phone and went to bed hoping that I would have some sort of erotic dream about Beth and her soft skin.

If you're like me, you probably thought that everyone in the world knows the Heimlich Maneuver, or at least they know to punch a choker in the gut. That's what I thought, anyway. Which is why I'm done with stories, have been done with the whole writing thing, and unlike my boy Ike, may he dress the beef, I start with chainsaws.

The body needs time to adjust to the new diet, and reorient the bodily functions to take in an excrete the new materials without doing damage to the organs or soft tissues. I'm in training and so I don't do much but sleep and eat and…excrete. Some have asked me how I do it, others wonder just how badly a person needs to fail at regular life to end up like me. My answer to both is the same, "Until you feel a four-inch iron bolt move through the inside of your body, towing a chainsaw rip-cord behind it, you have not experienced what it means to be alive.

.